MY GREAT BRITISH MAKE IT Bake it BOOK

SAMANTHA MEREDITH
SALLY MORGAN

SCHOLASTIC

Scholastic Children's Books,
Euston House, 24 Eversholt Street,
London NW1 1DB, UK

A division of Scholastic Ltd
London ~ New York ~ Toronto
Sydney ~ Auckland ~ Mexico City
New Delhi ~ Hong Kong

Editor: Elizabeth Scoggins

Published in the UK by Scholastic Ltd, 2014

Illustrated by Samantha Meredith
The material in this book is compiled from
The Great British Colouring Book (2012), *The Great British Activity Book* (2013)
The Great British Holiday Book (2013), *The Great British Christmas Book* (2013)
and *Great British Things to Make and Do* and *Great British Things to Bake and Do*
written by Sally Morgan (2014)

ISBN 978 1407 15288 2

Printed in Malaysia.

2 4 6 8 10 9 7 5 3 1

THIS GREAT BRITISH
BOOK BELONGS TO

CONTENTS

Things to Make

Things to Bake

Things to Colour and Doodle

Things to Do

Puzzles to Solve

GINGERBREAD PEOPLE

It is said that the first gingerbread people were made for Elizabeth I, who asked her cooks to shape gingerbread to look like her favourite guests.

Ingredients

- 350 g plain flour, plus extra for dusting
- 6 tsp ground ginger
- 1 tsp bicarbonate of soda
- 110 g butter, cut into cubes, plus extra for greasing
- 175 g soft brown sugar
- 5 tbsp golden syrup
- 1 egg, beaten
- a few currants.

Equipment

- Table knife, to cube the butter
- 2 bowls – 1 small, 1 large
- fork, to beat the egg
- 2 large baking trays
- kitchen paper
- rolling pin
- gingerbread person cutter.

1. Ask an adult to preheat the oven to 180°C/gas mark 4.

Warning! *Make sure you ask an adult to help you whenever you'd like to use the oven.*

2. Use kitchen paper to grease two large baking trays with butter.

3. Put the flour, ginger, bicarbonate of soda and butter in a large bowl. Rub the butter into the dry ingredients with your fingertips until the mixture looks like breadcrumbs.

4. Pour in the sugar, syrup and egg and squash it all together until you have a firm dough.

5. Dust your work surface and rolling pin with the spare flour. Roll out the dough until it is 5 mm thick.

6. Use a gingerbread person cutter to cut out as many people as you can from your dough.

7. Press together any leftover dough, roll it out again and cut out as many biscuits as you can, so there's no wasted dough.

8. Place your gingerbread people on your greased baking tray. Press two currants into the head of each of your people, for eyes.

9. Ask an adult to put your baking trays into the oven for 10–12 minutes until the biscuits are light brown and then leave to cool.

Great British tip

Use icing and sweets to give your people some super-sweet outfits. Try out some designs on these gingerbread people with pens and pencils.

KITCHEN COOL

Design an ace apron and pair of oven gloves for your dream kitchen.

MAKE A BAKER'S APRON

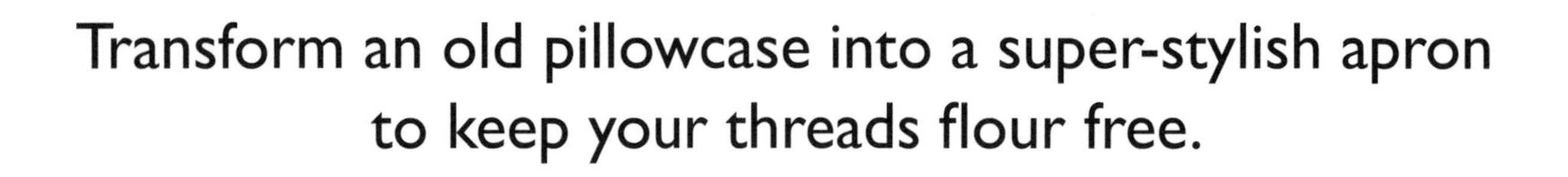

Transform an old pillowcase into a super-stylish apron to keep your threads flour free.

You will need

- Clean pillowcase
- ruler
- felt-tip pen
- 3 pieces of 70 cm-long ribbon
- scissors
- needle
- thread.

1. Turn the pillowcase inside out and lay it on a table, with the open end nearest to you.

2. Use a ruler to measure 12 cm in from each corner of the closed end, and mark with a felt-tip pen.

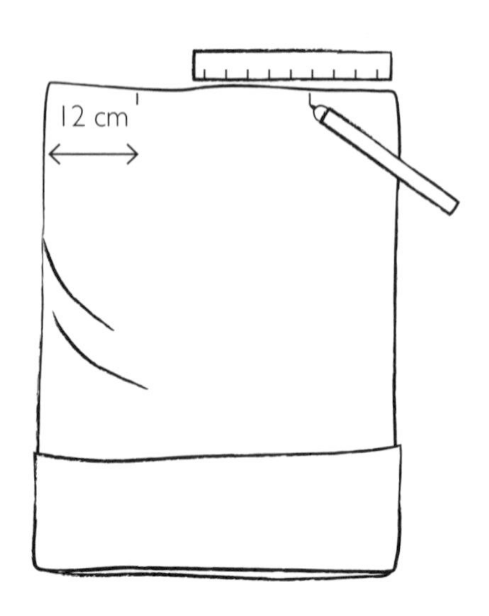

3. From each of your first marks, measure and draw a vertical line 20 cm long. Connect the bottom of each of these lines to the edge of your pillowcase, to make two rectangles.

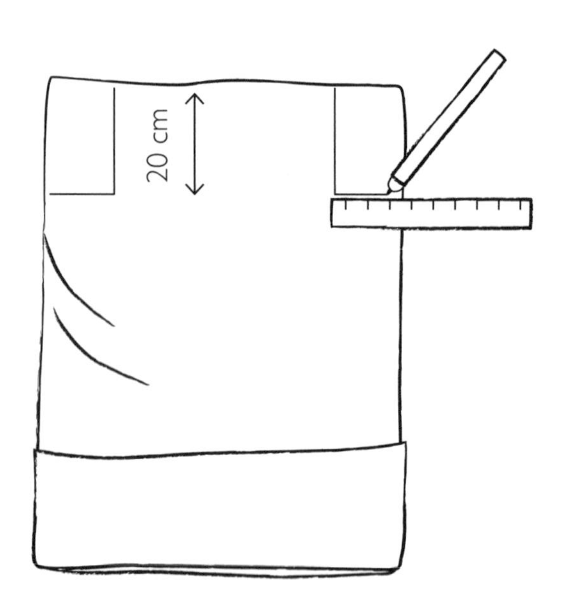

4. Draw another two lines 1.5 cm inside the lines already drawn to create two right angles, as shown by the dotted line.

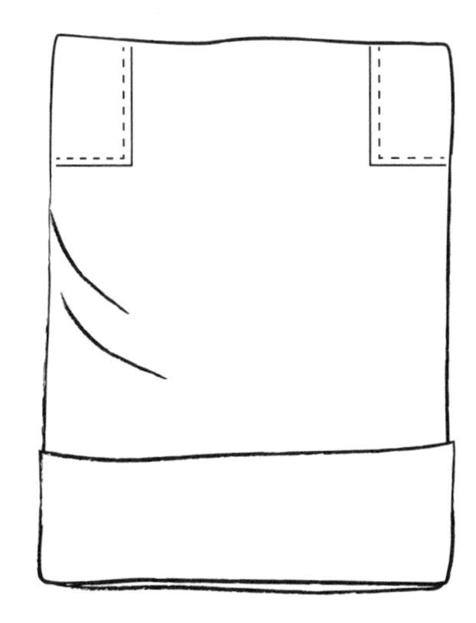

5. Cut out both of the smaller rectangles, leaving the first lines you drew showing on the pillowcase.

6. Using a needle and thread, sew down the longest line, then turn the corner and sew along the horizontal line. Secure your sewing with a few knots and snip away any excess thread. Repeat on the other corner. This will make sure your apron has neat edges. Now turn the pillowcase the right way round so it's no longer inside out.

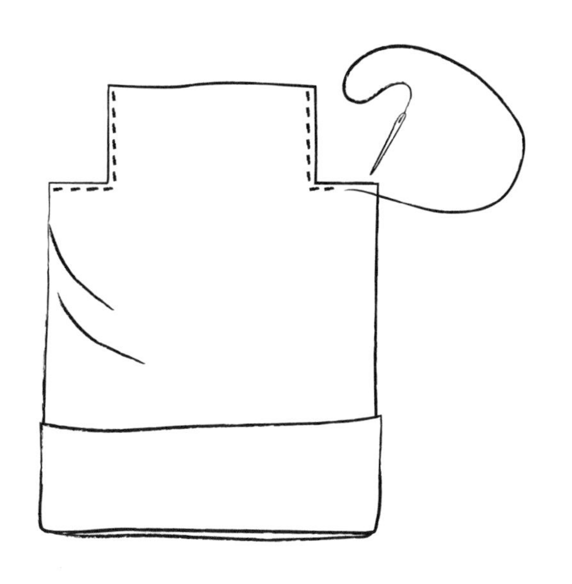

7. Take one piece of ribbon and stitch each end to the top corners of the back of your apron. This will form a loop that will go over your head.

8. Take the other two pieces of ribbon and stitch one to each of the centre corners of your pillowcase, as shown. These will tie around your waist.

Great British tip

Need your apron in a hurry? Instead of sewing your pinny together, try using fabric glue.

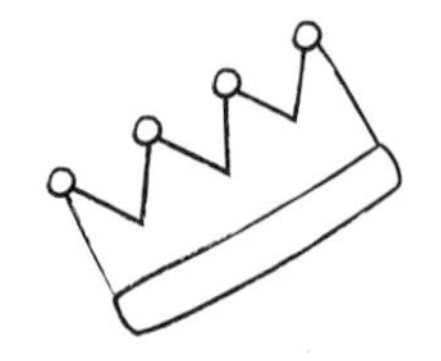

VICTORIA SPONGE

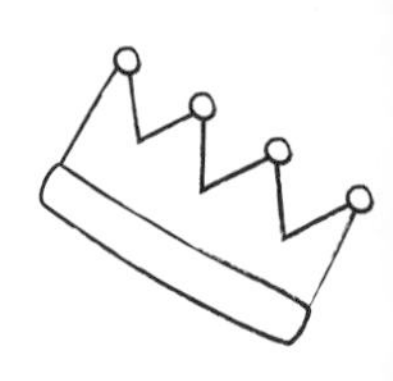

When you taste your jam-filled creation, you won't believe how easy it is to make.

Ingredients

- 200 g caster sugar
- 200 g butter, room temperature, plus extra for greasing
- 200 g self-raising flour
- 4 eggs, beaten
- 1 tsp baking powder
- 1 tsp vanilla extract
- 5 tbsp strawberry jam
- 2 tbsp icing sugar.

Equipment

- 2 bowls – 1 small, 1 large
- fork, to beat the eggs
- 2 x 20 cm round cake tins
- greaseproof paper
- pencil
- scissors
- wooden spoon
- sieve
- wire rack.

1. Ask an adult to preheat your oven to 190°C/gas mark 5.

Warning! *Make sure you ask an adult to help you whenever you'd like to use the oven.*

2. Use kitchen paper to grease your two cake tins with butter.

3. Fold a piece of greaseproof paper in half and place one of the cake tins on top. Draw around the tin with a pencil and cut out your circle. You will be left with two circles. Pop one onto the base of each tin.

4. Cream together your butter and sugar by mixing them with a wooden spoon in a large bowl, until the mixture is light and fluffy.

5. Beat the eggs into the mixture.

6. Next, sieve in the flour and fold it into the mixture by going all the way around the edge of the bowl once and then 'folding' the mixture on top of itself into the middle of the bowl. Repeat until all of the flour is mixed in.

7. Spoon half of the mixture into each tin and spread so it covers the base of the tin evenly.

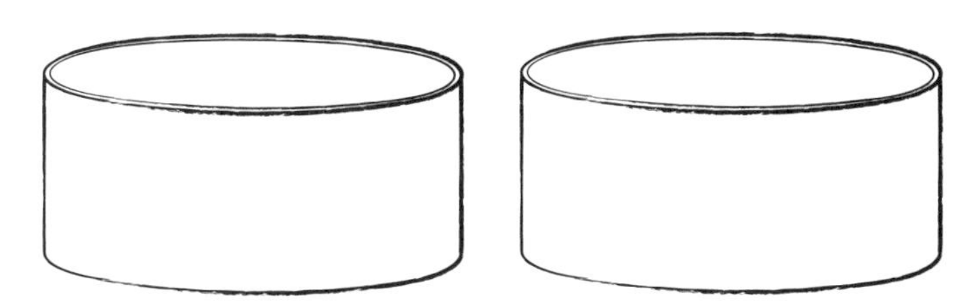

8. Ask an adult to put your tins into the oven for 20 minutes until they are a golden yellow colour.

9. Remove your cakes from the tins and place them on a wire rack until cool.

10. Spread the top of one of your cakes with jam and place the other cake on top.

11. Sprinkle the top with icing sugar and enjoy!

Lucky number 13

Bakers used to get into trouble if they sold their customers light loaves, so they would avoid accidentally cheating people by giving them 13 loaves for every dozen (or 12) that they ordered. That is why a baker's dozen is 13 and not 12.

Victoria what?!

It wasn't just this yummy cake Queen Victoria put her name to. In her lifetime she had plums, peas, flowers, cities and even waterfalls named after her.

The sweet stuff

Ever wondered where sugar comes from? Most of the sugar in Britain comes from sugar beet – big lumpy root vegetables that look like giant parsnips. That doesn't mean it counts as a vegetable though!

ALL THE FUN OF THE FAIR!

Can you spot 10 differences between these two pictures?
The answers are all at the back of the book.

PERFECT PANCAKES

Celebrate Shrove Tuesday by whipping up a batch of home-made pancakes.

You will need

- 225 g plain flour
- 2 eggs, beaten
- 600 ml milk
- knob of butter
- salt.

1. Sift the flour into a large bowl, add a pinch of salt and stir.

2. Pour in the beaten eggs and whisk the mixture until there are no lumps.

3. Slowly pour in the milk and stir. Cover the bowl and leave the mixture to stand for 30 minutes.

4. Ask an adult to put a non-stick frying pan over a high heat. Add the butter and let it melt.

Warning! *Make sure you ask an adult to help you whenever you'd like to use the hob.*

5. Spoon some of your mixture into the pan and swirl the pan around until the base is covered in pancake batter.

6. When the top of the batter has set, shake the pan to loosen your pancake and flip it over to cook the other side for one minute.

7. Tip onto a plate and add a topping of your choice.

Great British tip
Pancakes taste best smothered in fresh lemon juice and sugar.

SPLASH OF COLOUR

Rainbows aren't the only brightly coloured things that a good shower can make. The next time the clouds gather get creative with this unique gift wrap.

You will need

- empty salt and pepper pots
- powder paints
- newspaper
- a tray
- thick absorbent paper.

1. Unscrew the tops of the salt and pepper pots and fill each pot with a different colour of powder paint. Screw the tops back on.

2. Lay some newspaper down on the floor near your front or back door. Put your tray on the newspaper and place the piece of absorbent paper onto the tray.

3. Shake your pots over your paper to cover them with a light dusting of powder paint.

4. Put on your raincoat, carefully lift up the tray and take it outside. Lay your tray somewhere flat where it will get a good shower of rain. Leave it out in the rain for ten minutes.

5. Bring in your paper, lay it on some fresh newspaper and leave to dry. Save the paper to make a present look extra special. You can even make gift tags out of it.

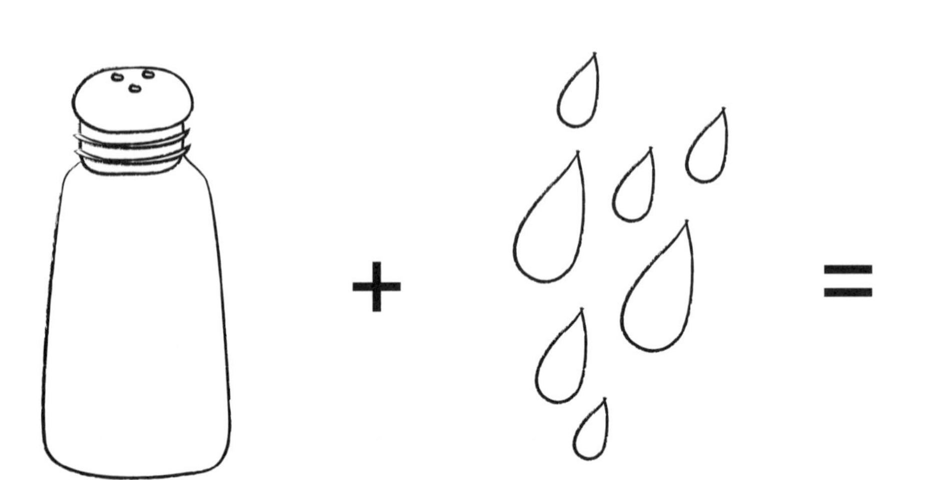

WOW-FACTOR WELLIES

Give an old pair of Wellington boots the wow factor and stop the rain from ruining your festival look.

You will need

- Wellington boots
- warm soapy water
- scrubbing brush
- paper
- pencil
- paintbrush
- acrylic paints.

1. Wash your wellies using plenty of warm soapy water. Remove any mud and stones from the soles using a scrubbing brush. Rinse and leave to dry.

2. While your boots dry, plan your design on paper. If your boots are red, you could paint black spots on them to turn them into ladybird boots or if they are green, you could paint on scales and eyes and turn them into a pair of dino boots. Let your imagination run wild.

3. Paint your design onto your boots. Leave them to dry. and wait for the rain!

Great British tip
Why wait for a festival? Put on your new boots and find the nearest puddle.

Give these brollies brilliant designs.

CLOCK PATIENCE

Here's a solo card game that will make any boring rainy day much more fun!

All you need to play is a standard pack of cards and a flat surface.

1. Shuffle a pack of cards until they're all mixed up. Then place 13 cards, face down, in the pattern of a clock. One card for the centre, and the rest in a circle.

2. Do this three more times, so that you have 13 piles of cards, with four cards in each pile.

3. To start, turn over the top card of the centre pile, as shown:

4. Place the card, face up, on the pile it matches. Aces for 1 o'clock, Jacks for 11 o'clock and Queens for 12 o'clock.

5. If you uncover a King, place it by the centre pile and turn over the top card again.

6. To win, you must uncover all the cards around the edge of the clock before you find all four Kings.

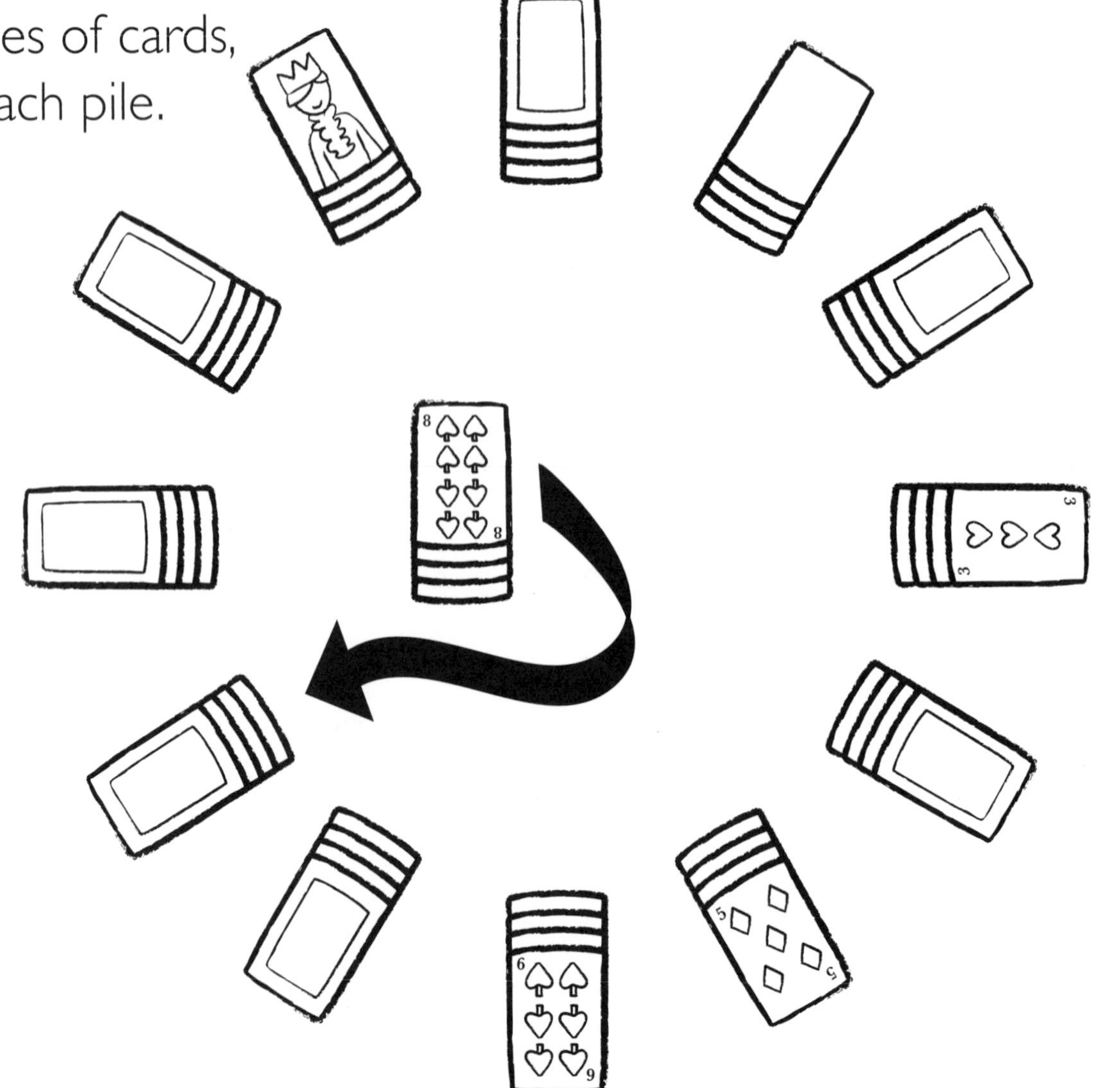

ST DAVID'S DAY

Celebrate St David's Day, the patron saint of Wales, on March 1st by making your own daffodil button-hole to wear.

You will need

- a cardboard egg box
- scissors
- paper
- a sharp pencil
- card
- a paintbrush
- yellow paint
- modelling clay
- a green pipe cleaner
- sticky tape
- a glue stick
- a safety pin.

1. Cut off one of the egg cups from the cardboard egg box. Trim around the top with scissors to neaten the edges.

2. Trace over the flower and circle templates on the opposite page using a pencil and piece of paper and cut them out.

3. Draw around your templates on a piece of card and cut them out.

4. Paint the cup from your egg box, the cardboard flower and the circle yellow and leave them to dry.

5. Ask an adult to place the egg cup on the piece of modelling clay and make a hole in the centre by pushing a sharp pencil through the middle into the clay. Repeat this to make a hole in the centre of your flower.

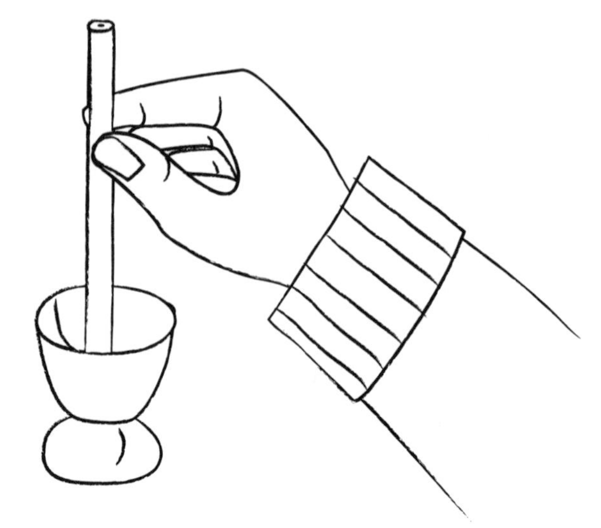

6. Push the end of the pipe cleaner through the hole in the flower and then through the hole in the egg cup, from the outside. Fold over 2 cm of pipe cleaner inside the cup and secure with sticky tape. Bend the pipe cleaner so your daffodil is facing forwards.

7. Apply glue to the back of the yellow circle and stick it in the centre of the egg cup to cover the end of the pipe cleaner. Leave it to dry.

8. Pin your daffodil to your chest and wear it with pride.

TOOT! TOOT!

Can you spot 10 differences between these two pictures?

ECCLES CAKES

Eccles cakes come from a town called Eccles in north-west England but their flaky yumminess is enjoyed all over Great Britain.

Ingredients

- 75 g butter, plus extra for greasing
- 150 g brown sugar
- 200 g dried mixed fruit
- 1 tsp cinnamon
- ½ tsp nutmeg
- 2 tbsp orange juice
- 500 g ready-made puff pastry
- 2 tbsp milk
- 1 tbsp granulated sugar
- a little flour, for dusting.

Equipment

- Large baking tray
- kitchen paper
- saucepan
- large bowl
- wooden spoon
- rolling pin
- 7 cm circular cutter
- teaspoon
- pastry brush
- table knife.

1. Ask an adult to preheat the oven to 200°C/gas mark 6.

> **Warning!** *Make sure you ask an adult to help you whenever you'd like to use the oven.*

2. Use kitchen paper to grease a large baking tray with butter.

3. Ask an adult to slowly melt the butter in a saucepan. Remove from the heat.

4. Put the sugar, fruit, cinnamon, nutmeg and orange juice into a bowl and carefully add the melted butter. Mix everything together with a wooden spoon.

5. Sprinkle flour onto your work surface and rolling pin, and lay your pastry on top. Roll out the pastry until it's roughly 3 mm thick.

6. Using a 7 cm circular cutter, cut out as many circles from the pastry as you can.

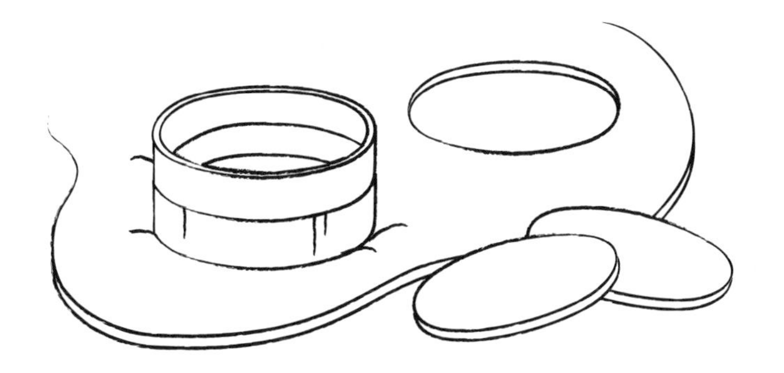

7. Press any leftover pastry together, roll it out again and cut out more circles until you have an even number, so there is no wasted pastry. You might need to add more flour to the rolling pin and the work surface if your pastry is too sticky.

8. Move half your circles onto the baking tray, and place a heaped teaspoonful of fruit mix into the centre of each one. Then, using a pastry brush, brush around the edges of the pastry with milk.

9. Place the rest of the circles on top of the fruit and press around the edges with your fingertips to seal them.

10. Make three slits in the top with a table knife and then brush each cake with a little milk.

11. Sprinkle the top of each cake with sugar.

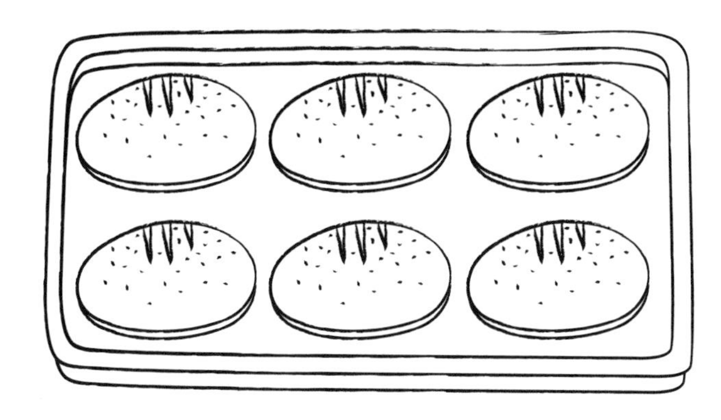

12. Ask an adult to put your baking tray in the oven for around 15 minutes, when the cakes should be crisp and golden.

13. Leave to cool for at least 15 minutes, then tuck in!

MOTHERS' DAY MAGIC

Make your Mum feel extra-special this Mothers' Day by getting her to put her feet up and have home-made afternoon tea.

Afternoon tea stand

You will need

- 3 large paper plates
- 2 paper cups
- a sharp pencil
- a lump of modelling clay
- 150 cm gift ribbon
- sticky tape
- scissors.

1. Ask an adult to place a paper plate onto the piece of modelling clay and push a sharp pencil through the middle to make a hole. Repeat this for each of the paper plates and the paper cups.

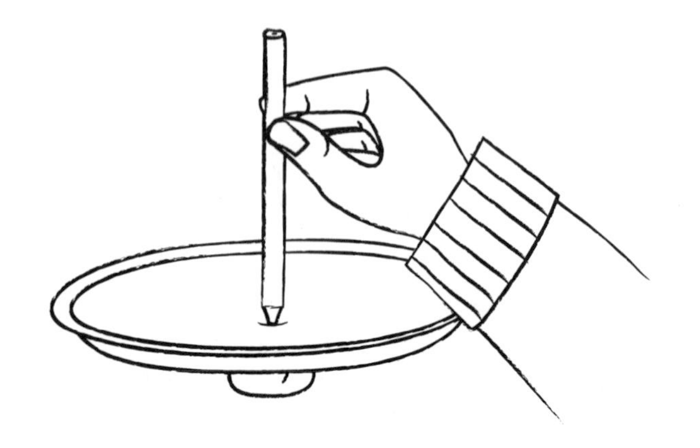

2. Fold the ribbon in half and thread the folded part through the hole in the underside of a large plate. Secure the ends of ribbon with sticky tape to the bottom of the plate.

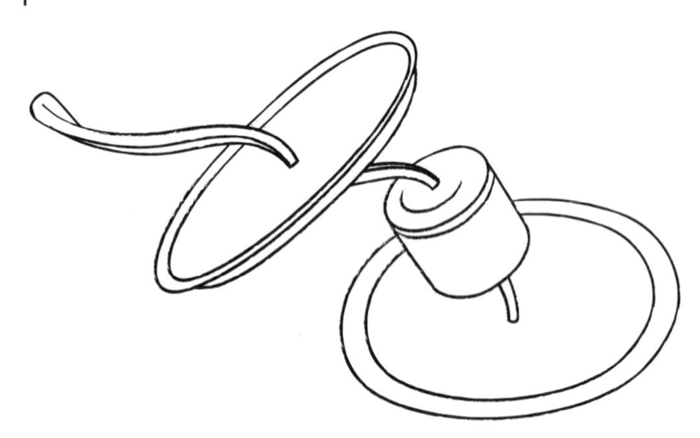

3. Continue to thread the ribbon from the top of the plate, through the hole in the cup and then through the underside of the other large paper plate. Repeat for the second cup and the last plate.

4. Cut the ribbon at the fold and tie with a knot.

To make finger sandwiches

You will need

- 150 g cream cheese
- 1 tbsp mayonnaise
- salt and pepper
- 3 slices wholemeal bread
- ½ cucumber, sliced
- 3 slices white bread.

1. Put the cream cheese, mayonnaise and a pinch of salt and pepper in a bowl and mix together.

2. Spread the mixture onto one side of each slice of wholemeal bread.

3. Lay the cucumber slices on top of the mixture.

4. Place the white slices of bread on top of the cucumber.

5. Cut the crusts off the sandwiches using a table knife. Cut each sandwich into four triangles.

6. Arrange on your afternoon tea stand, so that a brown side is next to a white side.

HOT CROSS BUNS

Nothing says springtime in Great Britain more than hot cross buns!

Ingredients

- 200 ml milk
- 50 g butter, plus extra for greasing
- 500 g strong white bread flour
- 3 tsp mixed spice
- 50 g caster sugar
- 7 g sachet of fast-action yeast
- pinch of salt
- 2 eggs, beaten
- 200 g currants
- 75 g plain flour, plus extra for dusting
- 4 tbsp water
- 1 tbsp golden syrup.

Equipment

- 3 bowls – 2 small, 1 large
- fork, to beat the egg
- large baking tray
- kitchen paper
- saucepan
- wooden spoon
- 2 tea towels
- sandwich bag
- pastry brush.

Warning! *Make sure you ask an adult to help you whenever you'd like to use the hob or the oven.*

1. Use kitchen paper to grease a large baking tray with butter.

2. Ask an adult to bring the milk to the boil in a saucepan, then remove it from the heat. Add the butter and stir until it melts. Leave to cool for 10 minutes.

3. Mix the strong white bread flour, spice, sugar, yeast and salt together in a large bowl. Pour in the warm milk and butter mixture. Add the beaten eggs and stir until you have a sticky dough.

4. Sprinkle the spare flour onto your work surface and put the dough on top of it. Knead the dough by squashing and squeezing it between your hands and against the work surface for 10 minutes, until it is smooth and squashy.

5. Put the dough back into your bowl and cover with a tea towel. Leave in a warm place for 1 hour.

6. Take the tea towel off the bowl. The dough should have doubled in size.

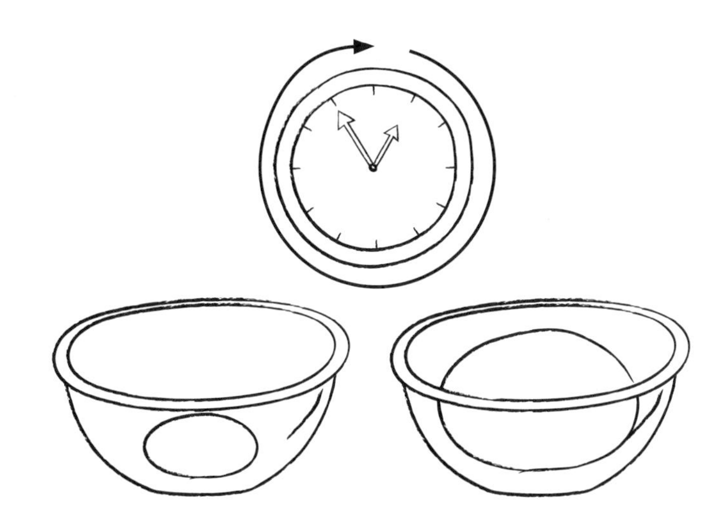

7. Tip in your currants and knead the dough again until the fruit is all mixed in.

8. Split your dough into 12 equal pieces and shape them into balls by rolling them between your palms. Place the balls of dough onto your baking tray, 5 cm apart. Cover with a clean tea towel and leave in a warm place for 1 hour.

9. Ask an adult to preheat the oven to 220°C/gas mark 7.

10. For the icing, mix the plain flour and the water in a small bowl and spoon into a sandwich bag. Carefully snip a small corner off the bag and gently squeeze two lines of flour paste onto the top of each bun to make a cross.

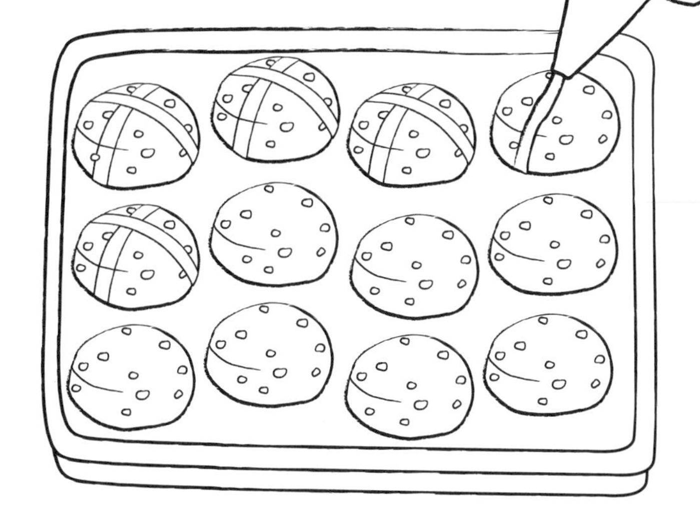

11. Ask an adult to pop your buns into the oven for 15 minutes, or until golden brown.

12. Brush with golden syrup and then leave to cool for 10 minutes. Split in half, spread with butter and enjoy.

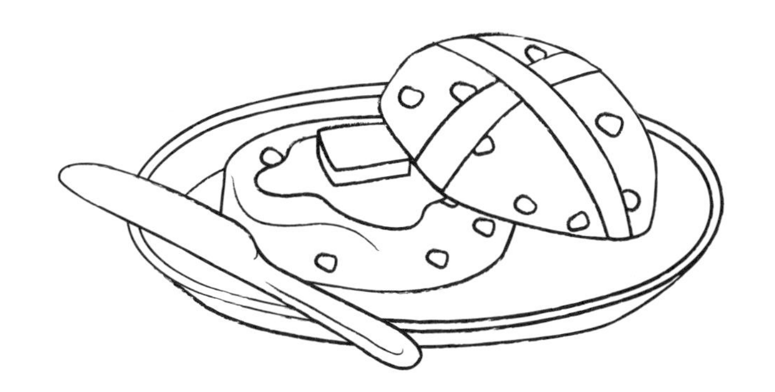

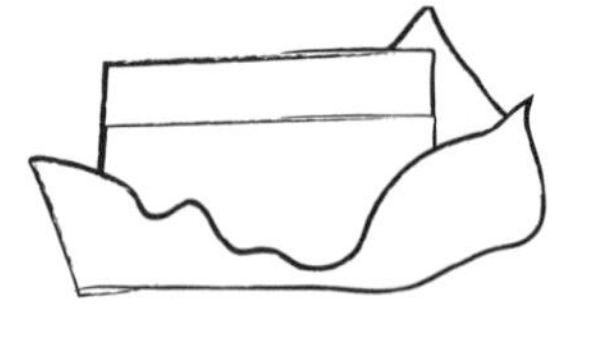

BREAD AND BUTTER PUDDING

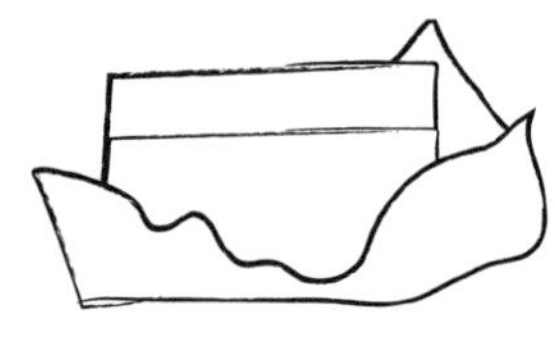

This yummy pudding is easy to make and a great way to use up any leftover hot cross buns or teacakes.

Ingredients
- 5 hot cross buns
- 50 g butter
- 50 g raisins
- 1 tin of custard (approx. 400g)
- 150 ml milk
- 2 tbsp light brown sugar.

Equipment
- Table knife
- ovenproof dish
- jug.

1. Ask an adult to preheat the oven to 200°C/gas mark 6.

2. Slice the buns in half and butter each half.

3. Cut the buns into quarters and then arrange neatly in the bottom of an ovenproof dish, butter-side down. Sprinkle your raisins over the top.

Warning! *Make sure you ask an adult to help you whenever you'd like to use the oven.*

4. Pour the custard into a jug, add the milk and stir together.

5. Pour the mixture over the buns, making sure they are completely covered. Sprinkle sugar over the top.

6. Ask an adult to put your pudding into the oven for 35 minutes, until the top is golden brown and crispy.

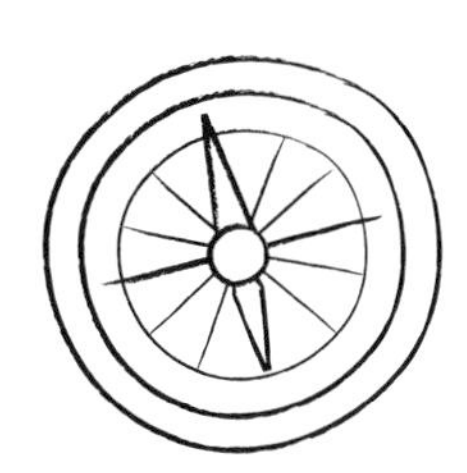

HOT CROSS MAZE

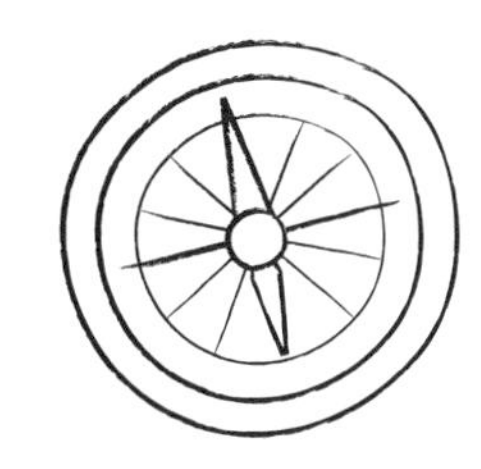

Can you find your way to the other side of this delicious tray of buns? Careful, they're hot!

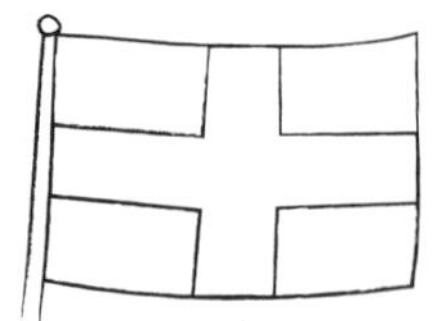

ST GEORGE'S DAY

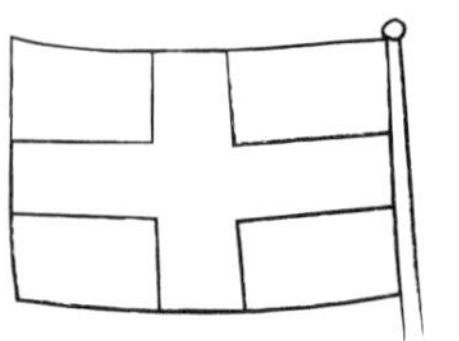

Celebrate St George's Day, on April 23rd, by putting on your very own St George and the dragon finger-puppet show.

You will need

- colouring pencils
- scissors.

1. Colour in the two puppets on the opposite page.

2. Turn the page over and colour in the other side.

3. Cut out your puppets using scissors. Take extra care when cutting out the circles for your fingers to go through.

4. Insert the index finger and middle finger on your right hand into the holes at the bottom of the dragon puppet. Do the same with your left hand with the holes in the St George puppet.

5. Put on a show! In the legend, George slays the dragon, but you can rewrite the story in any way that you like.

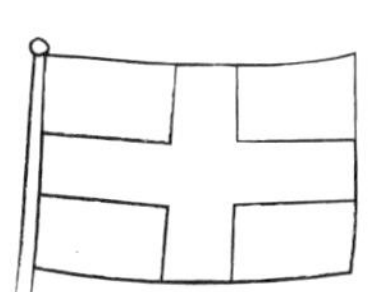

I-SPY ENGLAND

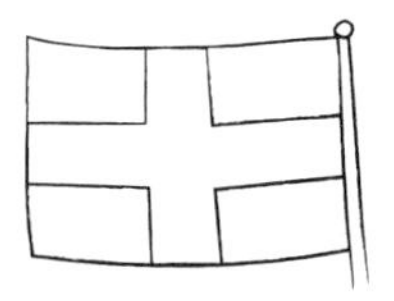

How many of these famous English things can you spy when you are out and about in England?

English flag	Black taxi cab	Red rose	Oak tree	Red phone box
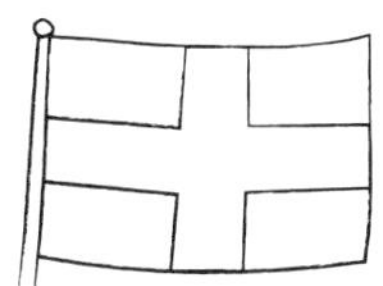				

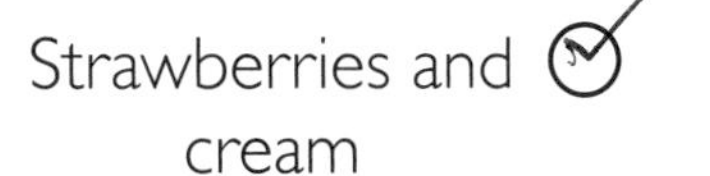

Thatched cottage	Strawberries and cream	Morris dancer	Cornish pasty	Underground station
	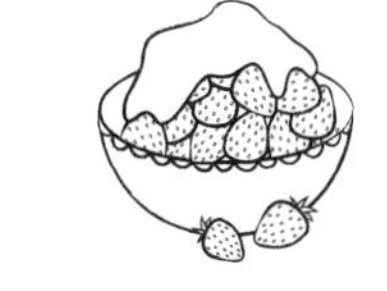			

Red post box	Double-decker bus	Beefeater	Game of cricket	Lion statue

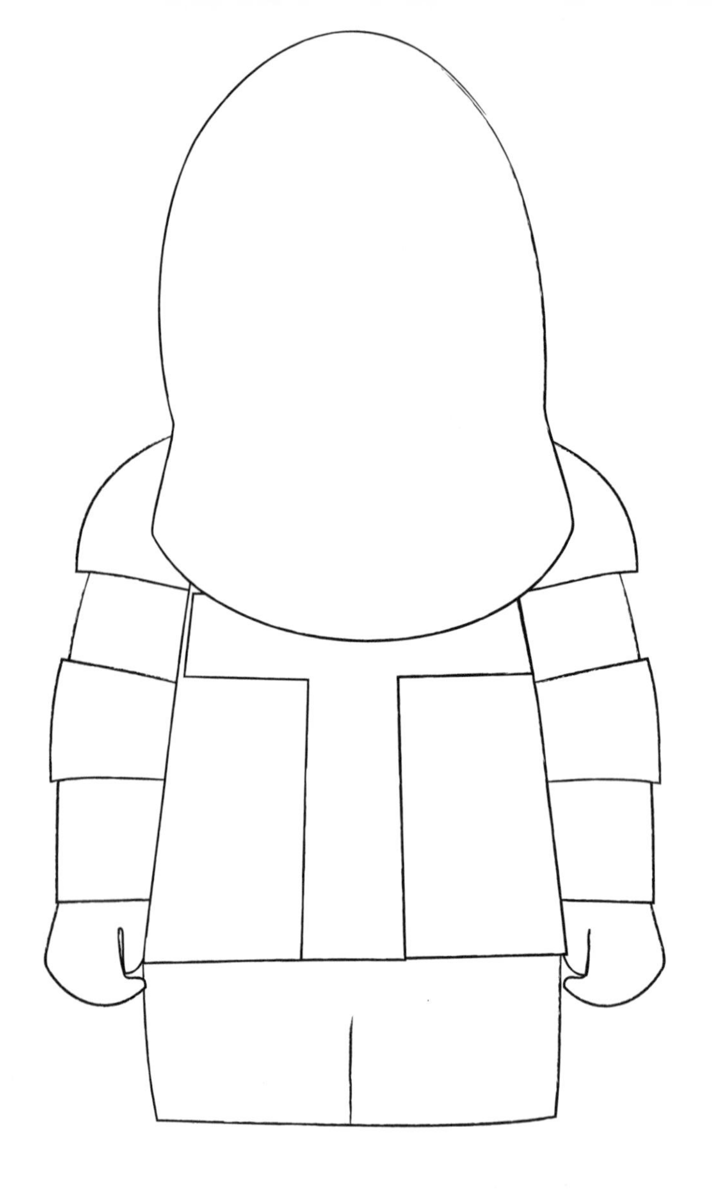

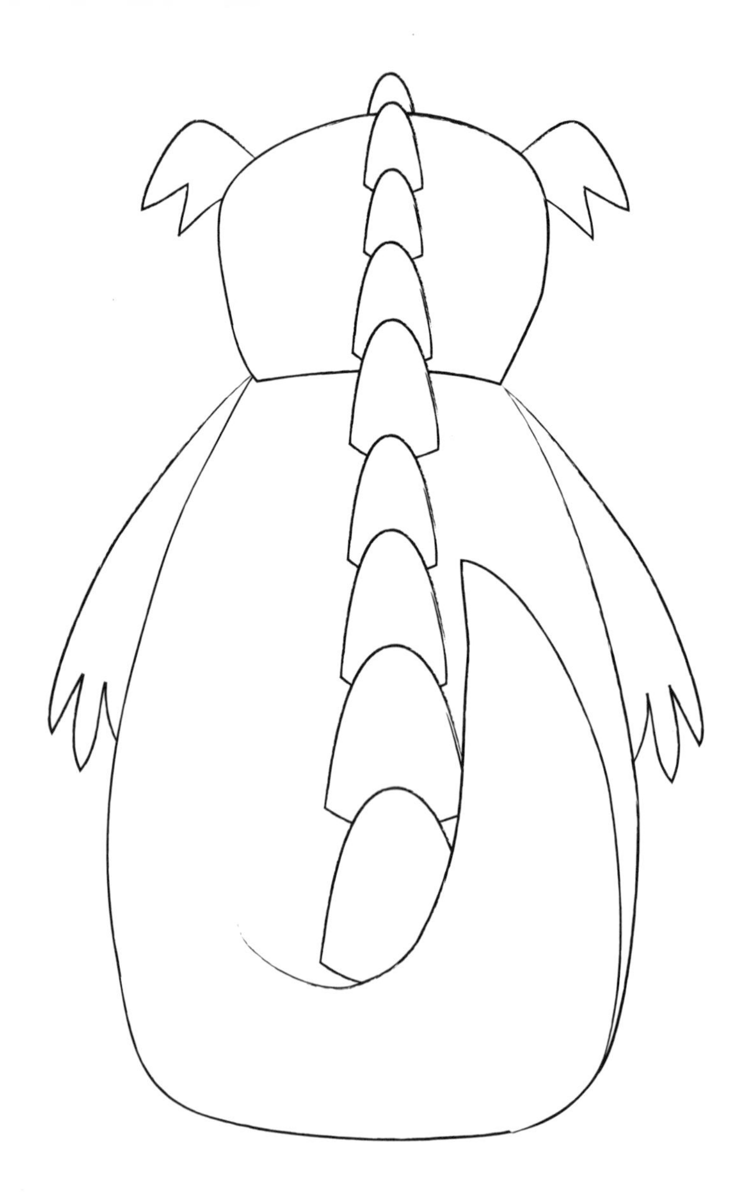

DRAGON QUEST

Can you complete the dragon quest and find all six dragons hiding in this valley?

SHREWSBURY BISCUITS

These fruity biscuits come from Shrewsbury, in the West Midlands. They are mentioned in cookbooks as early as the 1650s.

Ingredients

- 125 g butter, room temperature, plus extra for greasing
- 150 g caster sugar
- 2 egg yolks
- 225 g plain flour, plus extra for dusting
- 75 g currants
- 1 tbsp lemon zest, grated.

Equipment

- Grater, for the zest
- 2 large baking trays
- kitchen paper
- large bowl
- wooden spoon
- rolling pin
- 6 cm circular fluted cutter.

1. Ask an adult to preheat the oven to 180°C/gas mark 4.

2. Use kitchen paper to grease two large baking trays with butter.

Warning! *Make sure you ask an adult to help you whenever you'd like to use the oven.*

3. Cream the butter and sugar together in a large bowl with a wooden spoon until the mixture is light and fluffy.

4. Add the egg yolks and stir until they are all mixed in.

5. Stir in the flour, lemon zest and currants until you have a crumbly dough that you can squash together with your hands.

6. Sprinkle flour onto your work surface and rolling pin and put the dough on top of it. Roll out the dough until it is 0.5 cm thick.

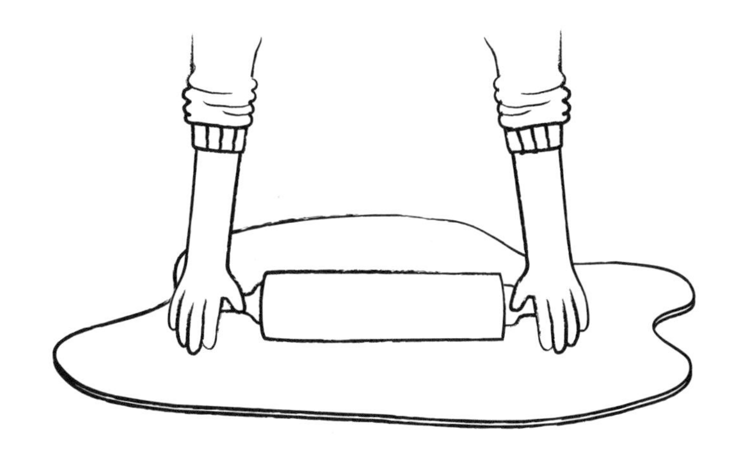

7. Use your circular fluted cutter (one with crinkly edges) to cut out as many biscuits as you can from the dough.

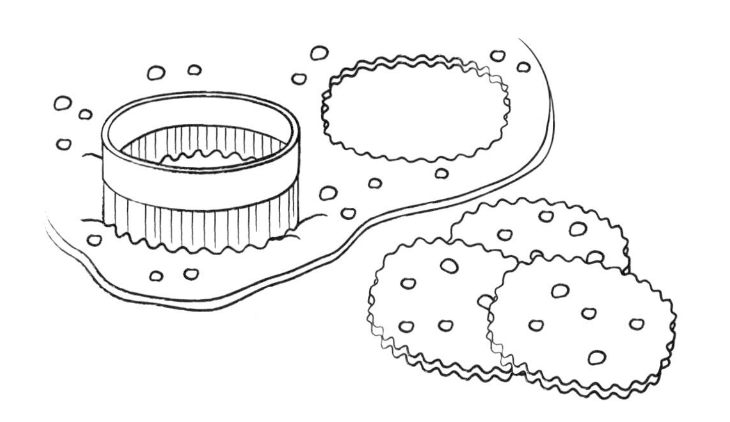

8. Press together any leftover dough, then roll it out again and cut out more biscuits until you've used up all of the dough so there's none wasted.

9. Place the biscuits onto the baking trays and ask an adult to put them in the oven for 15 minutes, or until they are beginning to turn a pale golden colour.

10. Leave to cool and enjoy.

Great British tip

If you store your biscuits in an air-tight container, like an old sweet tin or a Tupperware, they will last a lot longer.

Colour the bunting ready for a street party …

... then add
your own designs.

FUN AT THE FÊTE

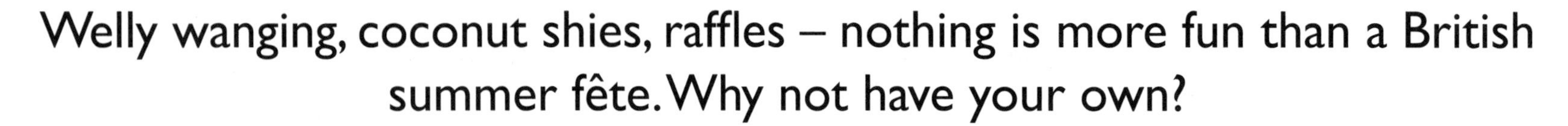

Welly wanging, coconut shies, raffles – nothing is more fun than a British summer fête. Why not have your own?

Coconut shy

You will need

- 6 empty toilet rolls
- paint
- paintbrushes
- newspaper
- masking tape
- tennis balls.

1. Paint your toilet rolls in bold, bright colours and leave to dry.

2. Take a large sheet of newspaper and scrunch it up into a ball shape. Cover the outside of your ball in masking tape to hold it together. Repeat to make five balls.

3. Paint your newspaper balls with brown paint. Experiment with different shades to get a textured effect like the outside of a coconut. Leave to dry.

4. Stand your toilet rolls on their ends and line them up on a table or against a wall. Balance a paper coconut on the top of each toilet roll.

5. To play, each player takes it in turns to stand 3 metres away from the line of 'coconuts' and throws three tennis balls to try to knock over as many as they can.

Wang a Welly

You will need

- a stick
- a Wellington boot
- stones.

1. Lay the stick horizontally on the ground. Each player must stand behind this marker when they take their turn.

2. From behind the marker, each player must throw the Wellington boot as far as they can, three times.

3. Use the stones to mark where the Wellington boot lands.

4. The winner is the player who throws the welly furthest.

Ways to Wang

Try different throwing techniques to see what works best for you.

Backwards

Stand with your back to the marker, hold your welly in both hands, bend your knees and swing it between your legs, then up and over your head, and let go.

Underarm

Stand facing forwards, hold the welly out in front of you and then, keeping your arm straight, swing it back and then forward as quickly as you can and release the welly.

The Hammer Toss

Give the game a twist, by throwing your welly like the hammer in the Highland Games. Spin around on the spot, just behind the marker. When you are going really fast, and are facing the marker, release your welly.

PLAY TIME!

Sevens is a brilliant game with seven steps, which you can play by yourself or with friends. All you need is a small, bouncy ball, such as a tennis ball, and a wall to bounce it against. Here's how to play:

1. Stand away from the wall, throw the ball at the wall and catch it.

2. Throw the ball at the wall, but let it bounce before you catch it.

3. Throw the ball at the wall, use your hand to whack it back at the wall, then catch it.

4. Repeat step **3**, but this time let the ball bounce before you catch it.

5. Hit the ball at the wall, let it bounce, whack it back then catch it.

6. Repeat step **5**, but bounce the ball on the ground before you catch it.

7. Lastly, repeat step **6**, but bounce the ball on the ground twice at the end before you catch it.

Try the steps again, but add a twist before you throw. You can:

- Clap your hands
- Clap twice
- Spin on the spot
- Only use your right hand
- Only use your left hand
- Throw the ball under one leg
- Throw the ball under the other leg.

PARTY BUNTING

Bunting is the perfect way to decorate for any holiday party – follow the instructions below to custom-make your own.

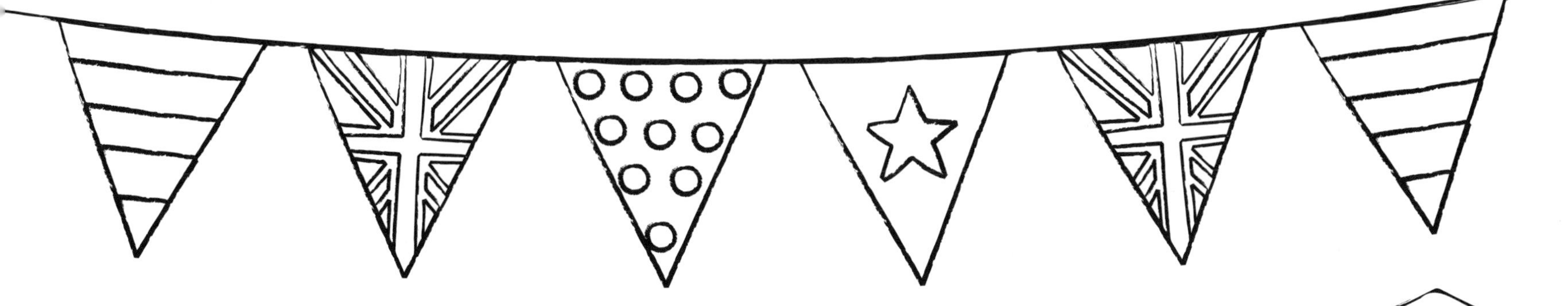

You will need

- scissors
- sheets of coloured paper
- a pencil
- bright marker pens or felt tips
- a roll of gift ribbon
- sticky tape.

1. First, cut carefully around the bunting shape above. This will be your template.

2. Place the template on a sheet of coloured paper and draw around it with your pencil.

3. Repeat, across the whole sheet, but make sure that none overlap.

4. Use your coloured pens to doodle designs all over your bunting shapes – try polka-dots, stripes or anything you like!

5. When you've finished, carefully cut out all the shapes around your pencil outline. You may need to do several sheets to make enough bunting pieces.

6. Fold each piece of bunting over between the two widest points.

7. Now cut a 2-metre length of ribbon and hook the bunting pieces onto it along the folds.

8. Secure each one in place with sticky tape. Remember to leave enough space at the ends of the ribbon to tie the bunting in place.

Have a great party!

FLAPJACKS

Chewy and oaty – perfect for walks in the countryside.

Ingredients

- 300 g butter, cut into cubes, plus extra for greasing
- 5 tbsp golden syrup
- 100 g soft brown sugar
- pinch of salt
- 500 g rolled oats.

Equipment

- Table knife, to cube the butter
- rectangular cake tin
- kitchen paper
- large saucepan
- wooden spoon.

1. Ask an adult to preheat the oven to 180°C/gas mark 4.

2. Use kitchen paper to grease the inside of a cake tin with butter.

3. Ask an adult to slowly melt the remaining butter (300g) in a large saucepan.

Warning! *Make sure you ask an adult to help you whenever you'd like to use the hob or the oven.*

4. Remove the saucepan from the heat. Add the syrup, sugar and salt and stir until all of the sugar has dissolved.

5. Add the oats and stir until they are coated with the sugary butter.

6. Spoon the mixture into your tin, pressing it into the corners and smoothing over the surface.

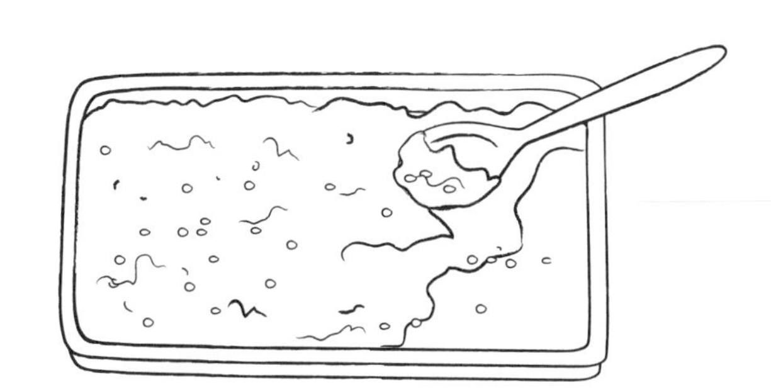

7. Ask an adult to put the tin into the oven for 25 minutes, or until the flapjack is golden.

8. Cut into rectangles using a table knife. Enjoy on a hike in the Great British outdoors.

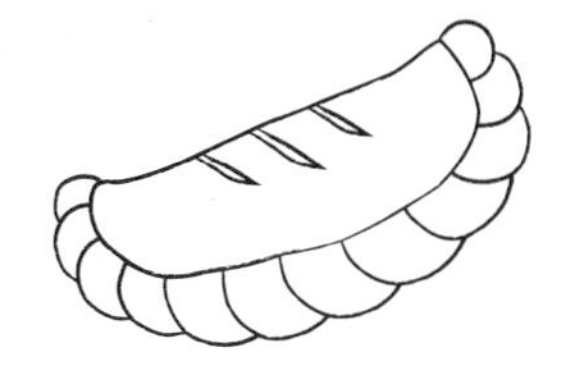

CORNISH PASTY

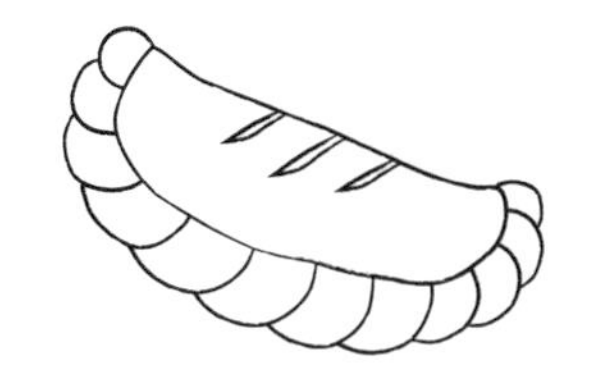

Make these traditional Cornish savoury treats, perfect for a spring or summer picnic.

You will need

- 740 g ready-rolled shortcrust pastry
- 1 tbsp plain flour
- 400 g chuck steak, chopped
- 1 onion, chopped
- 1 large baking potato, chopped
- ½ swede, chopped
- 1 egg, beaten
- pinch of salt and pepper.

1. Ask an adult to preheat the oven to 200 °C/gas mark 6.

2. Put the steak, onion, potato, swede, salt and pepper into a large bowl and mix together.

3. Sprinkle flour on your work surface and place a sheet of pastry on top. Lay a small plate on top of your pastry and cut around it using a table knife.

4. Spoon the mixture on to the right-hand side of your pastry circles, leaving a 3 cm gap around the edge of the pastry for the crust.

> **Warning!** *Make sure you ask an adult to help you whenever you'd like to use a sharp knife or the oven.*

5. Brush around the edge of each circle with egg. Fold the pastry in half to make a semi-circle. Press the edges together so no mixture leaks out.

6. Brush each of your pasties with egg to make them nice and shiny.

7. Place your pasties on a greased baking tray and ask an adult to put them in the oven for 15 minutes.

8. After 15 minutes, ask an adult to turn the oven down to 180 °C/gas mark 4 and bake for 40 minutes.

9. When the pasties are golden brown, leave to cool and enjoy.

LET'S GO!

Answer these questions and follow the answers to find out whether you're a Beach Buddy, Adventure Pal or City Chum.

START HERE

At the weekend, which would you rather do?

Get out and about on a bike. You hate to waste a single minute!

Which activity would you prefer to try?

Visit an interesting museum or gallery – there's so much to discover out there.

Which lessons do you prefer to do at school?

Wind-surfing
You're a great
Beach Buddy
– the perfect
person to hang
out with on
the sand.
Parachuting
P.E. and science
You're a
perfect
Adventure
Pal – you
like nothing more that
to fill your free-time with fun.
History and
English
You're an
ideal City Chum
– happy to spend
time visiting all the
most interesting
places you
can find.

PENNY RACERS

This game is a great to play on a journey or at home. Just follow the instructions below to get racing!

Attach a penny to a piece of sticky tack to make each counter, and borrow a dice from another game. To start, take turns to throw the dice (do this carefully if you are travelling) – the player with the highest number has the first go.

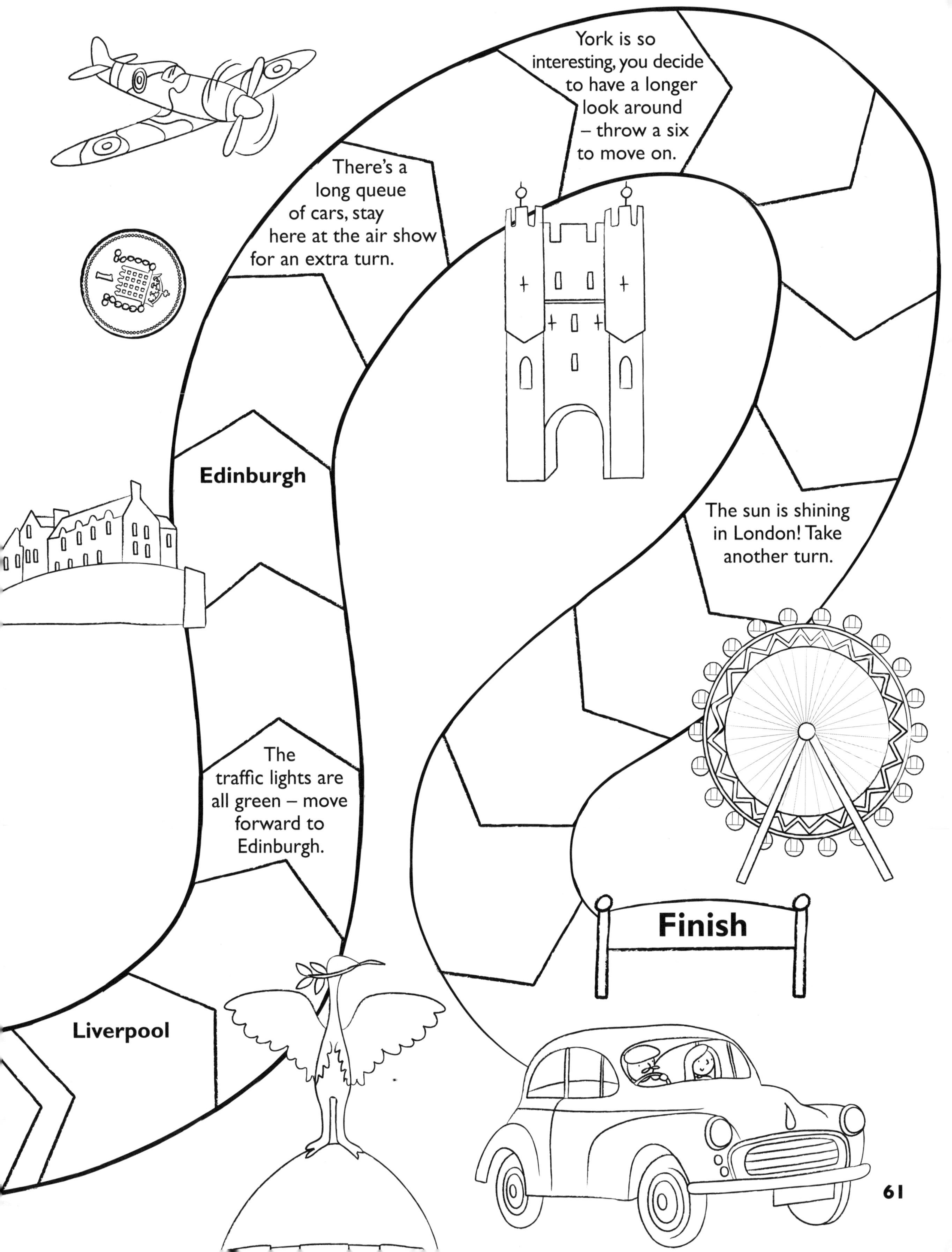
York is so interesting, you decide to have a longer look around – throw a six to move on.
There's a long queue of cars, stay here at the air show for an extra turn.
Edinburgh
The sun is shining in London! Take another turn.
The traffic lights are all green – move forward to Edinburgh.
Finish
Liverpool

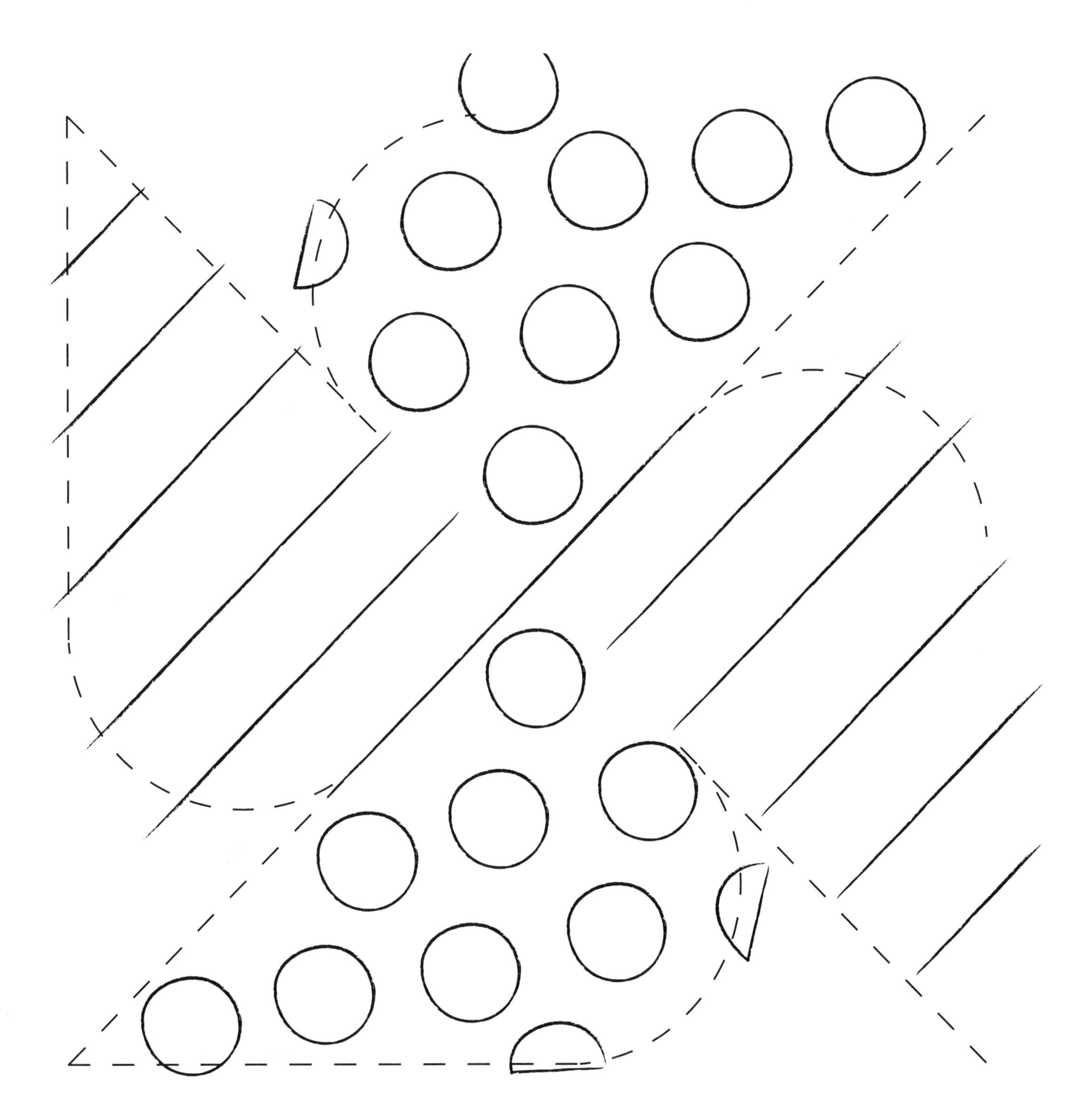

WINDMILL SPINNER

You will need

• pens or pencils
• scissors • a piece of sticky tack • a spare pencil
• a drawing pin.

Colour the pattern on both sides, then turn the page to find out how to make your windmill.

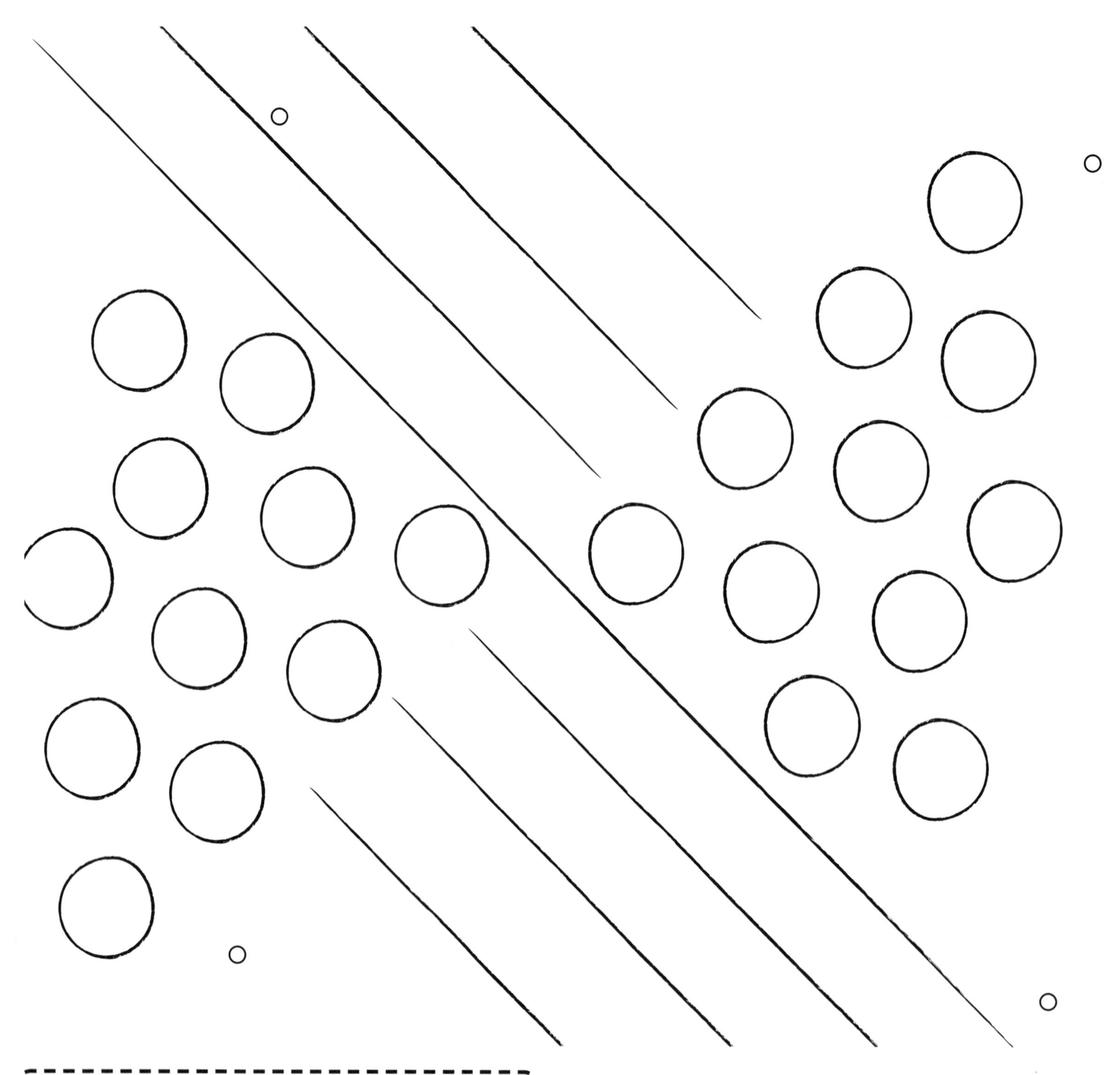

Warning! *Ask an adult to help you when you are using sharp objects.*

1. Cut along the dotted lines, so that you have a shape like this:

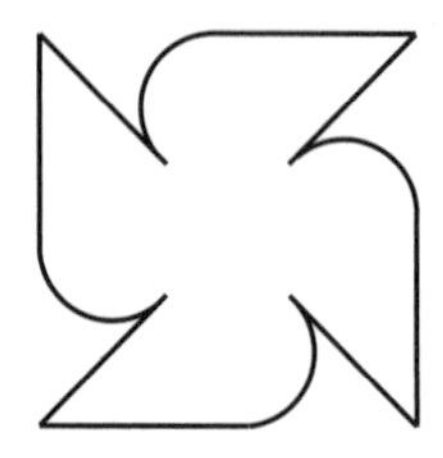

2. Place each small circle at the corners and centre over the sticky tack and make a hole with a pencil.

3. Bring the corners over to the centre, so the holes line up. Put the pin through the holes. Carefully push it into the pencil, and blow!

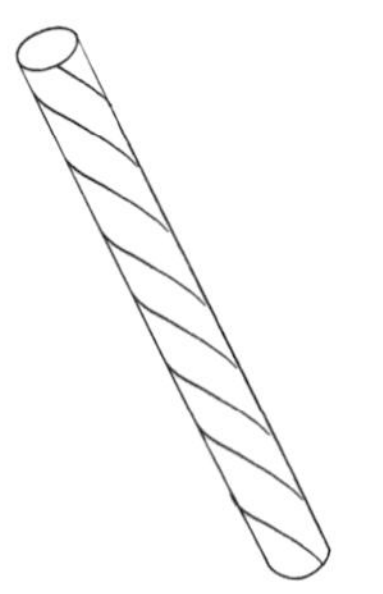

SEASIDE ROCK BISCUITS

Create minty biscuits with leftover sticks of rock.

Ingredients

- Broken sticks of rock
- 100 g butter, room temperature
- 150 g soft brown sugar
- 100 g granulated sugar
- 1 egg, beaten
- 190 g plain flour
- ½ teaspoon baking powder
- 100 g dark chocolate chips.

Equipment

- 3 bowls – 1 small, 2 large
- fork, to beat the egg
- 2 large baking trays
- sandwich bag
- rolling pin
- wooden spoon
- tablespoon
- wire rack.

1. Ask an adult to preheat the oven to 180°C/gas mark 4.

2. Line two large baking trays with greaseproof paper.

Warning! *Make sure you ask an adult to help you whenever you'd like to use the oven.*

3. Put the sticks of rock into a sandwich bag, seal, and crush with a rolling pin (being careful of your fingers!).

4. Place the butter and sugars in a large bowl and mix with a wooden spoon until the mixture is light and fluffy. Stir in the beaten eggs until it is all mixed in.

5. In another bowl, mix together the flour and baking powder.

6. Add the flour mix to the wet ingredients in the first bowl and stir until it is all mixed together.

7. Add the crushed rock and the chocolate chips and mix together gently until they are all combined.

8. Use a tablespoon to place dollops of mixture, the size of ping-pong balls, onto the paper-lined baking trays, 5 cm apart.

9. Ask an adult to put the trays into the oven for 15 minutes, then leave to cool on a wire rack.

How many sticks of rock can you find hidden in this seaside scene?

Decorate these sandcastles and doodle your own.

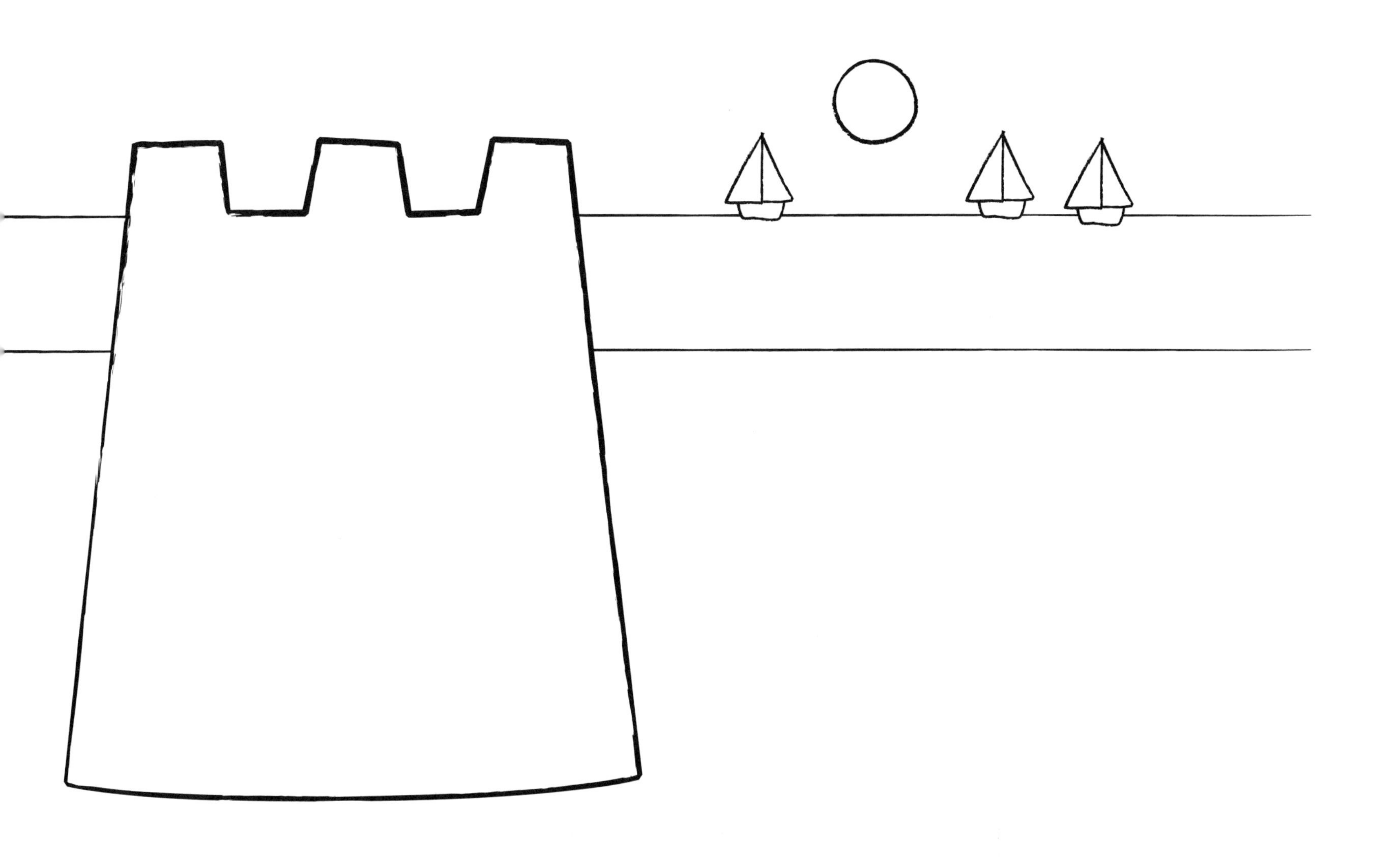

FOSSIL FINDING

Did you know that British beaches are a great place to find fossils?

Where to go?

- Dorset Coast, England
- North Yorkshire Coast, England
- Essex Coast, England
- Sutherland, Scotland
- Llantwit Major, Wales.

What to look for?

- Pick up any stones on the beach that look different or interesting. If any of your stones look like the pictures below, you've found a fossil

Warning! *Tides can change very quickly. Always check the local tide schedule before heading to the shore and take an adult with you.*

- If you see any irregular lumps or swirls on rocks these could be fossilized ammonites or even trilobites – extinct animals without backbones, known as invertebrates

- Look out for large flat areas of rock on the shore and see if you can find a series of regular dents in the stone. These could be dinosaur footprints from millions of years ago.

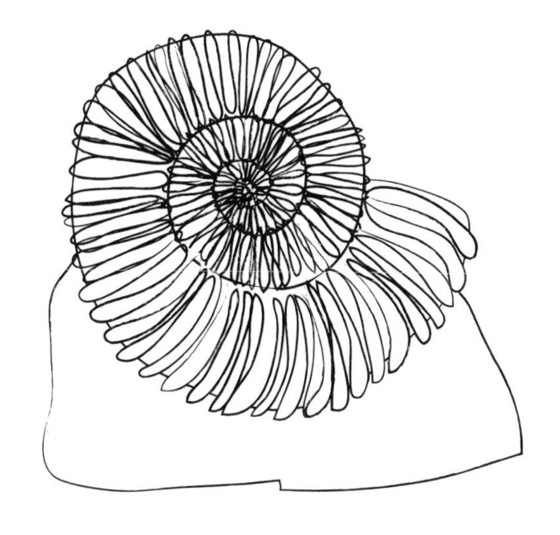

Ammonite

Fossilized sea urchin

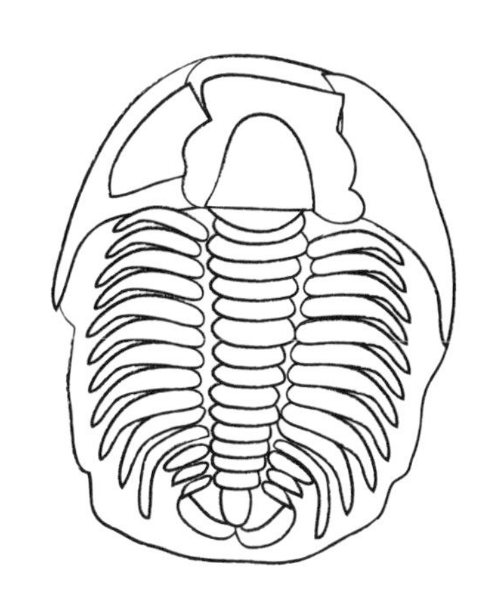

Trilobite

AWAY WE GO

When you just can't wait to get to where you're going, a brilliant travel game will make the journey much more fun.

Alphabet Packing

To begin the game, the first player says, "I went on holiday, and I took …" then picks an item starting with 'A' – an apple, for instance. The next player must remember that, then add an item starting with 'B': "I went on holiday, and I took an apple and a bag."

Each player must add an item starting with the next letter of the alphabet, without forgetting any that have gone before. If anyone forgets one, or can't think of an item for the next letter, they are out of the game.

Number-Plate Spotters

This game is great to play if you're in a car, coach or bus. All you need to do is spot the letters of the alphabet, in order, on any number plates that go by…

…You can either take it in turns with other players, or try it by yourself. Be warned though – some letters are much more unusual than others.

Beep!

Take turns to choose something that you can see for the other players to guess along the way. Choose something that you'll see again and again, such as lamp-posts, cows or cars with luggage on the roof.

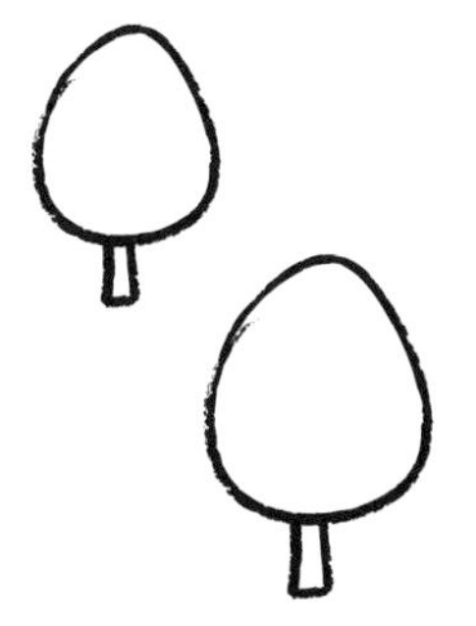

Each time you spot your chosen object, shout, "Beep!" and see how long it takes for someone to guess what it is. The first person to guess correctly takes a turn.

FABULOUS FAIRY CAKES

Fairy cakes are just like their American friends – cupcakes – but smaller and even easier to make.

Ingredients

- 265 g butter, room temperature
- 115 g caster sugar
- 2 eggs, beaten
- 1 tbsp milk
- 1 tsp vanilla essence
- 115 g self-raising flour
- ½ tsp baking powder
- 300 g icing sugar
- 2 tbsp milk.

Equipment

- 3 bowls – 1 small, 2 large
- fork, to beat the eggs
- wooden spoon
- whisk
- 2 x 12-hole bun tins
- paper cases
- teaspoon
- wire rack
- table knife.

Warning! *Make sure you ask an adult to help you whenever you'd like to use the oven.*

1. Ask an adult to preheat the oven to 180°C/gas mark 4.

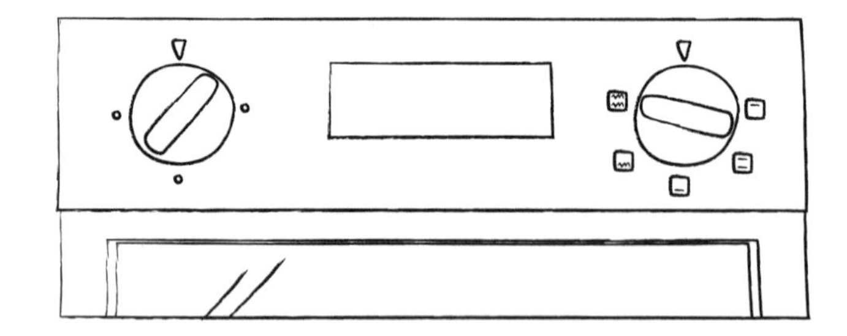

2. Put 115 g of your butter and all of the caster sugar into a large bowl. Mix with a wooden spoon until the mixture is light and fluffy.

3. Add the beaten eggs, milk and vanilla essence. Whisk together.

4. Add the flour and baking powder and whisk together until you have a smooth mixture.

5. Fill two 12-hole bun tins with paper cupcake cases. Use a teaspoon to half fill each of the cases with your mixture.

6. Ask an adult to put your fairy cakes into the oven for 10 minutes and leave to cool on a wire rack.

7. For the buttercream icing, put the rest of the butter (150 g) into a large bowl and beat with a wooden spoon until it is light, fluffy and a pale yellow colour.

8. Add 150 g of the icing sugar and stir until is all mixed in. Then add the rest of the icing sugar and mix together again.

9. Stir in the milk a little at a time until you have a smooth mixture.

10. Use a table knife to carefully cut a circle off the top of each of your cakes, creating a small hole. Put the spare pieces of cake to one side and fill the holes with a dollop of icing.

11. Using a table knife, cut each the spare piece of cake in half and push the two halves into the icing, so they look like wings.

Great British tip:
Make your fairy cakes extra special by adding food colouring to your icing with sprinkles on top.

PARTY PUZZLER

Everyone on Apple Blossom Avenue is ready for the street party to begin, but where are all the party hats?

Mrs Jones from number 12 was the last to have the hats, but she's been to lots of houses this morning. Can you work out where she left them?

First, she turned left out of her house and went three doors along to Bill and Katy's to borrow their plates. Next, she went to pick up Mrs Singh from the house opposite, then popped next door into the house with a tree outside it to collect some party-poppers. She's sure that's where the party hats are – do you think they are in number **3**, **4** or **7**?

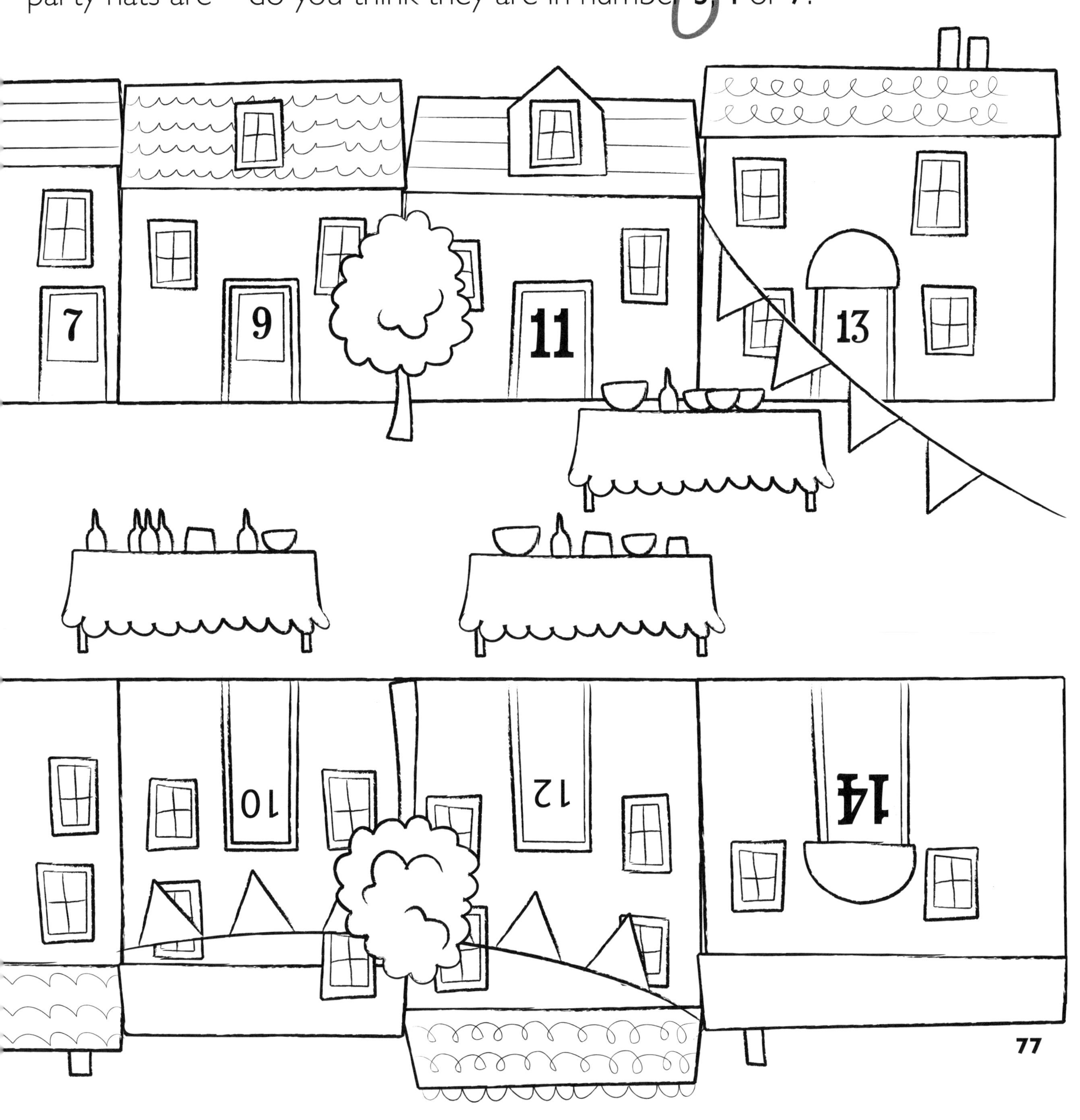

ETON MESS

This is one mess your parents will be happy you made in the kitchen this summer.

Ingredients

- 400 g strawberries
- 2 tsp caster sugar
- 500 ml whipping cream
- 8 meringue nests.

Equipment

- Table knife
- colander
- 2 large bowls
- whisk
- metal spoon.

1. Wash your strawberries in cold water. Cut off the stalks and cut the strawberries into quarters using a table knife. Put them in a bowl with the sugar.

2. In another bowl, whisk the cream until it can hold its shape on a spoon.

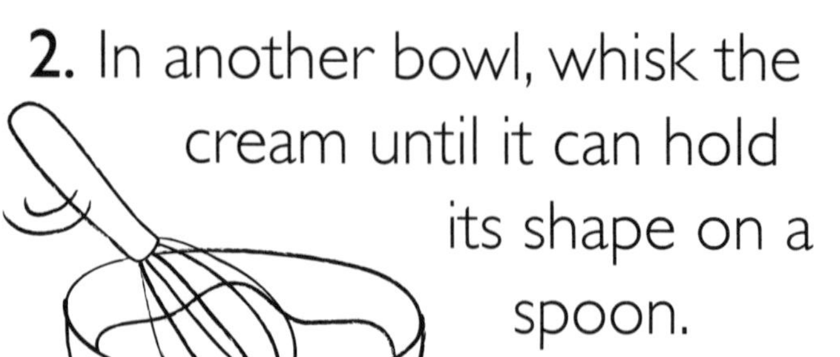

Great British tip

Whisking cream can take some time so you may want to ask an adult's help, or use an electric whisk.

3. Crumble the meringue nests into the cream. Don't worry if the pieces are uneven, it all adds to the mess!

4. Add your strawberries and sugar and mix everything together with a metal spoon. Take care not to mix too hard so you don't break up the meringue more than you have to.

5. Serve in a large pretty bowl or in individual glasses.

WHAT A MESS

Oh no! Amir's kitchen has got into a real state.
Can you help him find everything he needs to make his Eton mess?

10 × 8 × 2 × 2 × 1 × 2 × 6 ×

FLAG-TASTIC CAKE PLATTER

Serve your delicious cakes on a Union Jack cake platter.

You will need
- Dinner plate
- large cardboard box
- felt-tip pen
- scissors
- blue tissue paper
- 2 pieces of 30 x 4 cm white ribbon
- 2 pieces of 30 x 2 cm red ribbon
- sticky tape.

1. Place a dinner plate on one side of the cardboard box, draw around it with a felt-tip pen and carefully cut it out.

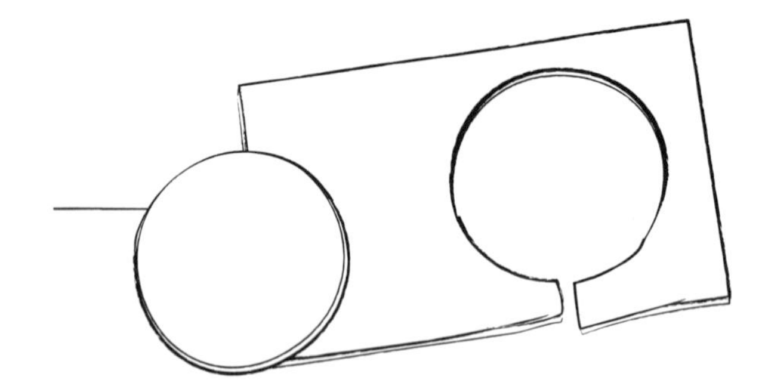

2. Cover one side of your circle with tissue paper and carefully secure it on the underside of the circle with sticky tape. Don't pull too tight or the paper might tear.

3. Take your white ribbon and arrange it on your circle in a diagonal cross. Lay the red ribbon over the top of the white ribbon, in the centre.

4. Tuck the ends of the ribbon under the cardboard circle, pull tight and secure to the underside with sticky tape.

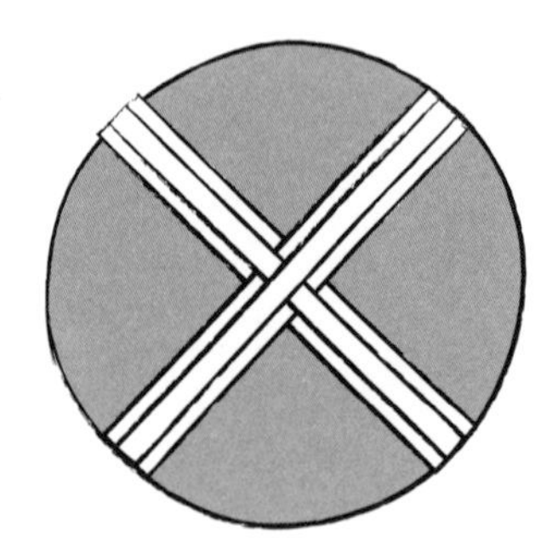

5. Next, lay the white ribbon over the top in a cross shape, placing the red ribbon on top of the white ribbon as before. Secure again with sticky tape.

6. Pile high with delicious baked goods.

FAIRY FINISHES

Decorate the icing and cases of these fairy cakes so they look yummy enough to eat!

FESTIVAL FUN

There's so much going on at the Edinburgh Festival! Can you spot ten differences between these two pictures?

CARNIVAL COLOURS

It's children's day at the Notting Hill Carnival in London so why not make your own magical mask and join the party?

You will need

- colouring pens or pencils
- scissors
- glue
- glitter
- sequins
- feathers (optional)
- clear hole reinforcements
- a sharp pencil
- modelling clay
- elastic
- sticky tape.

1. Colour in the masks on the opposite page lots of bright colours.

2. Cut them out. Take extra care with the eye holes.

3. Decorate your masks with glitter and sequins and, if you have them, glue feathers to the sides.

4. Ask an adult to make holes in your masks at the places marked, using a sharp pencil and modelling clay.

5. Stick one clear hole reinforcement around each hole.

6. Thread elastic through the holes in the masks and secure with a knot and sticky tape.

7. Put on your mask and your most colourful party clothes. Give your spare mask to a friend.

SUMMER LASSI

When things get hot this summer, what better way to cool down than with a delicious, Indian-inspired mango lassi?

You will need

- 250 ml plain yoghurt
- 125 ml semi-skimmed milk
- 250 g fresh mangoes, chopped
- 125 ml mango juice
- sugar
- ice cubes
- tall glasses.

1. Place your glasses into the freezer to chill.

2. Put all of your ingredients, except the sugar and ice cubes, into a blender and ask an adult to blend it until all of the mango has broken up and mixed into the yoghurt and milk.

3. Have a taste of your lassi. Mangoes are very sweet, but if you think your drink could use more sweetness, add a little sugar and blend again.

4. Take your glasses out of the freezer and put a few ice cubes into the bottom of each one. Pour in your smooth summer lassi and enjoy with thirsty friends.

Great British tip
Why stop at mango? Experiment with any fruit that takes your fancy. Slurrrrp-tastic!

TOTTENHAM CAKE

Squares of Tottenham cake used to be sold for a penny each! They are utterly delicious no matter which football team you support.

Ingredients

- 225 g butter, room temperature, plus extra for greasing
- 225 g caster sugar
- 4 eggs, beaten
- 280 g self-raising flour
- 2 ½ tsp baking powder
- 2 tsp lemon zest, grated
- 4 tbsp milk
- 300 g icing sugar
- 5–6 tbsp water
- 1 drop pink food colouring.

Equipment

- 3 bowls – 2 small, 1 large
- fork, to beat the eggs
- grater, for the zest
- 35 x 25 cm rectangular cake tin
- kitchen paper
- greaseproof paper
- scissors
- 2 spoons – 1 wooden, 1 metal
- wire rack
- palette knife
- table knife.

Warning! *Make sure you ask an adult to help you whenever you'd like to use the oven.*

1. Ask an adult to preheat your oven to 180°C/gas mark 4.

2. Use kitchen paper to grease the inside of a cake tin with butter. Line it with greaseproof paper.

3. Cream together the butter and sugar in a large bowl by mixing them with a wooden spoon until the mixture is light and fluffy.

4. Add the beaten eggs and beat them into the mixture.

5. Add the flour and baking powder. Fold them into the mixture by going all the way around the edge of the bowl once and then 'folding' the mixture on top of itself into the middle of the bowl. Repeat until all of the flour is mixed in.

6. Finally, add the lemon zest and milk and stir well.

7. Spoon the mix into your tin. Smooth it out with a metal spoon.

8. Ask an adult to put the tin into the oven for 35 minutes, or until golden. Remove from the oven and leave on a wire rack to cool.

9. For the icing, put your icing sugar into a small bowl and add a little water at a time, until you have a smooth runny paste. Add the food colouring and stir until you have an even pink colour.

10. Once the cake is cool, turn it the right way up and pour the icing over your cake. Spread it evenly over the top and sides using a palette knife. Leave to set.

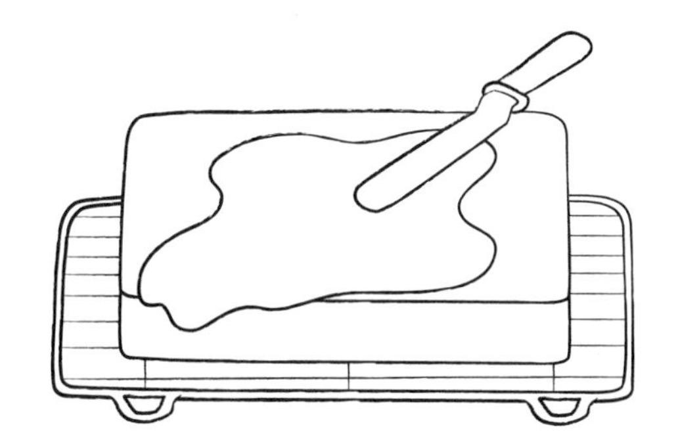

11. Cut your cake into squares using a table knife and enjoy while watching the football.

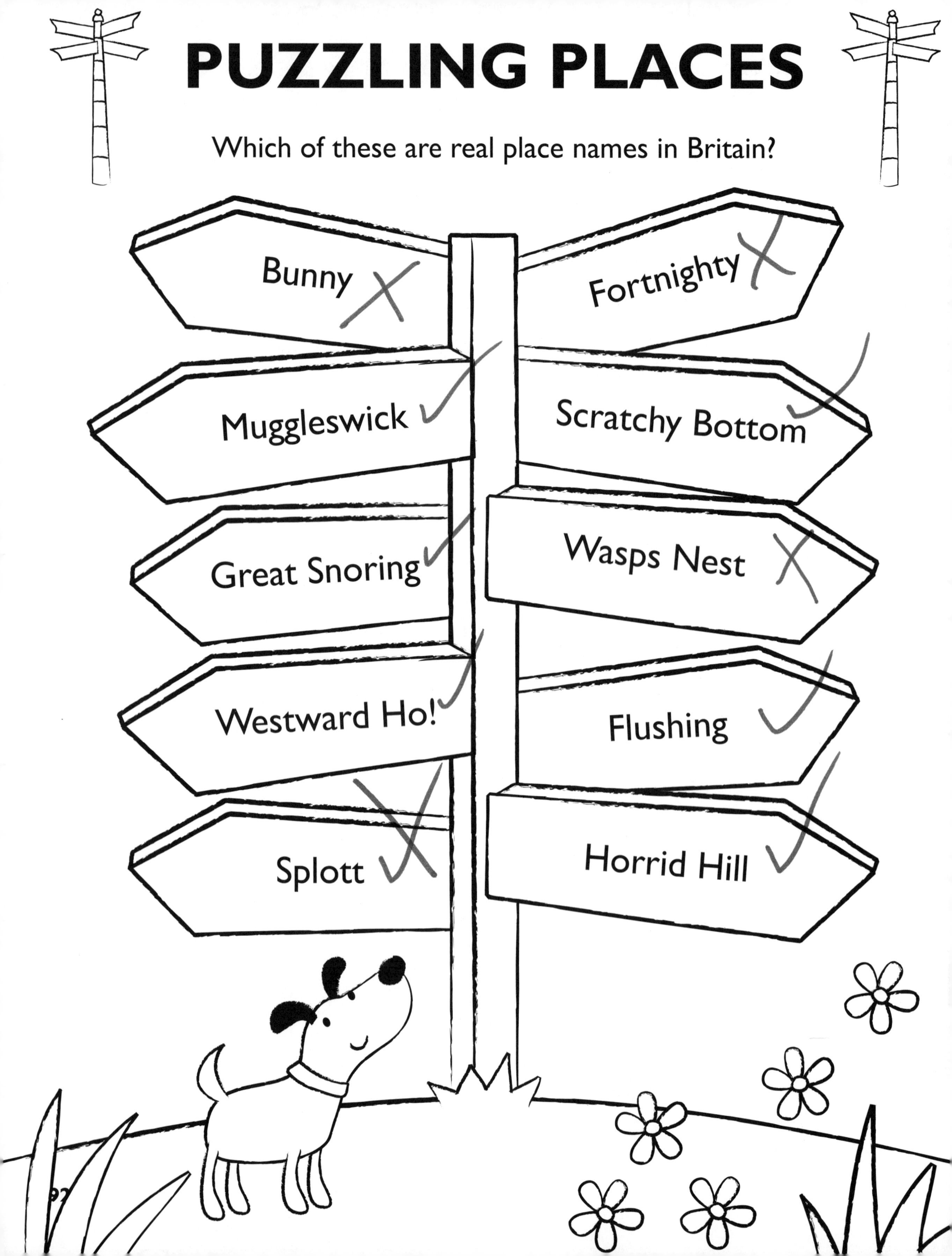
PUZZLING PLACES
Which of these are real place names in Britain?
Bunny
Fortnighty
Muggleswick
Scratchy Bottom
Great Snoring
Wasps Nest
Westward Ho!
Flushing
Splott
Horrid Hill

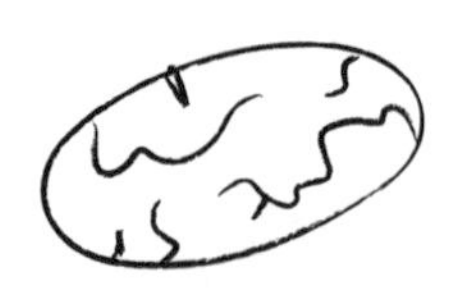

CORNISH FAIRINGS

These spicy little biscuits used to be sold at fairs all over Cornwall. They are delicious with a glass of cold milk.

Ingredients

- 225 g plain flour
- 2 tsp baking powder
- 1 ½ tsp baking soda
- 1 tsp mixed spice
- 1 tsp cinnamon
- 2 tsp ground ginger
- 100 g butter, cut into cubes
- 1 whole lemon zest, grated
- 100 g caster sugar
- 4 ½ tbsp golden syrup.

Equipment

- Table knife, to cube the butter
- grater, for the zest
- large baking tray
- greaseproof paper
- large bowl
- wooden spoon
- tablespoon.

1. Ask an adult to preheat the oven to 180°C/gas mark 4.

2. Take a large baking tray and line it with greaseproof paper.

Warning! *Make sure you ask an adult to help you whenever you'd like to use the oven.*

3. Pour the flour, baking powder, baking soda and spices into a large bowl and mix together well.

4. Add the butter and use your fingertips to rub it into the flour until there are no large lumps of butter left. Your bowl should look like it is full of crumbs. Add the zest and the sugar and stir well.

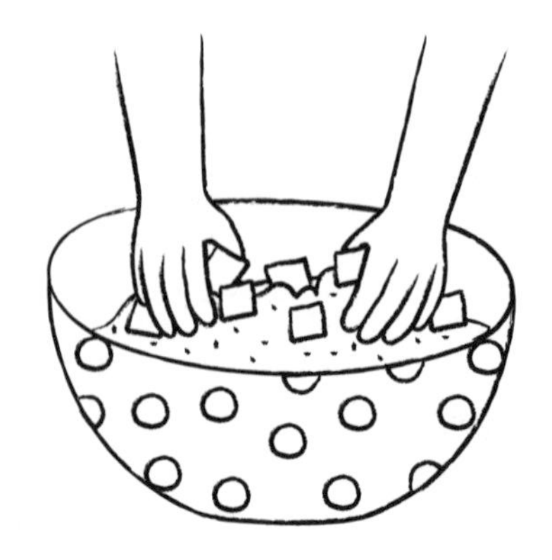

5. Add the syrup and mix together with your hands until you have a soft dough.

6. Use a tablespoon to take lumps of dough and shape them into walnut-sized balls between your palms.

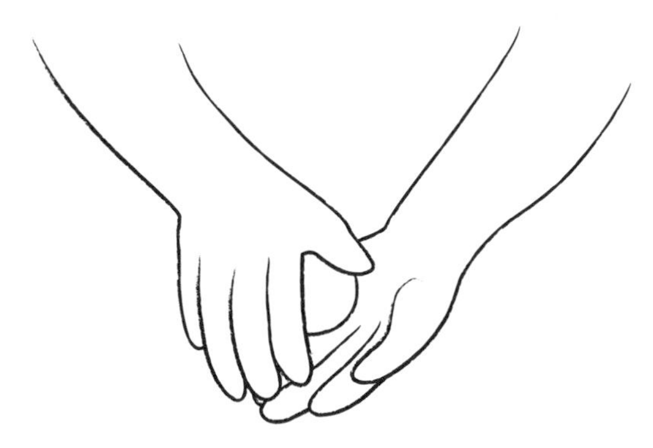

7. Place the dough balls on your baking tray, 5 cm apart.

8. Ask an adult to put the baking tray into the oven for 10 minutes, until they have spread out into golden, crackle-topped biscuits. Leave to cool and enjoy.

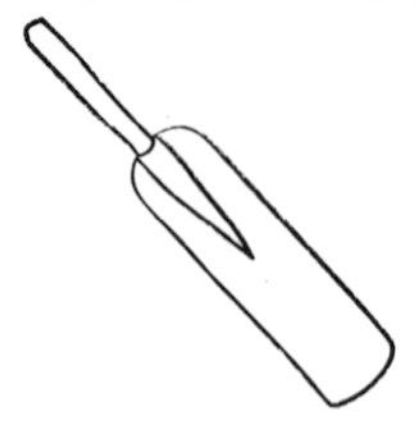

GARDEN CRICKET

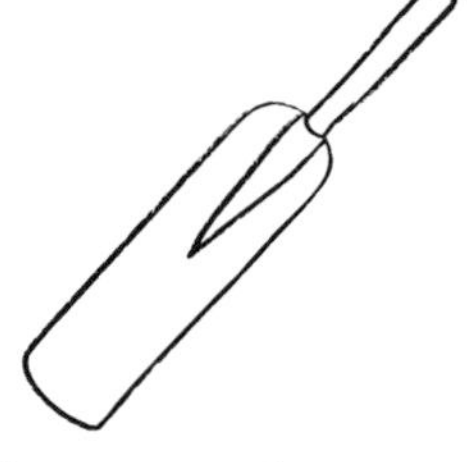

Grab a bat, some friends and head out into the garden or park to play a game of garden cricket. It's fast and super-easy to learn.

You will need
- cricket bat or tennis racket
- tennis ball or other soft ball
- 3+ players.

1. Decide who will bat and who will bowl first. The rest of the players will be the fielders.

2. The batter must take the bat, walk 5 metres away from the bowler and hold the bat in front of his or her legs. The batter's legs act as the stumps would in real cricket.

3. The batter must stay on the same spot at all times. They're allowed to turn to face the other way but they can't move from the position they first stand in.

4. The bowler throws the ball, underarm or overarm, at the batter's legs and the batter tries to hit it as far as possible. If the bowler hits the batter's legs, the batter is out and it's the bowler's turn to bat.

5. If a fielder or the bowler catches a hit ball, before it touches the ground, they must shout 'How's that!'. It is then their turn to bat. If a fielder or the bowler doesn't catch the ball, they must bowl from where the ball lands.

6. The game continues until you want to stop. The winner is the player who was batting longest.

Up, up and away! Colour these balloons and design your own.

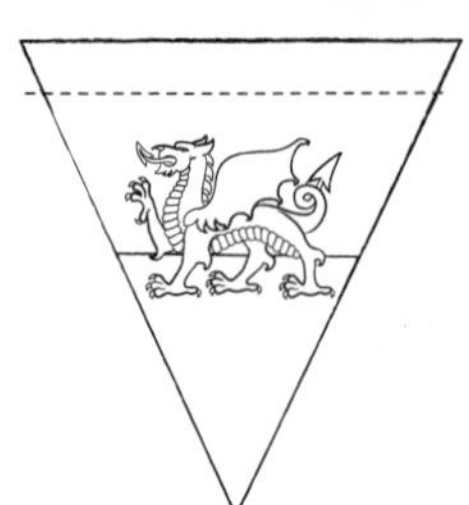

FLY YOUR FLAGS

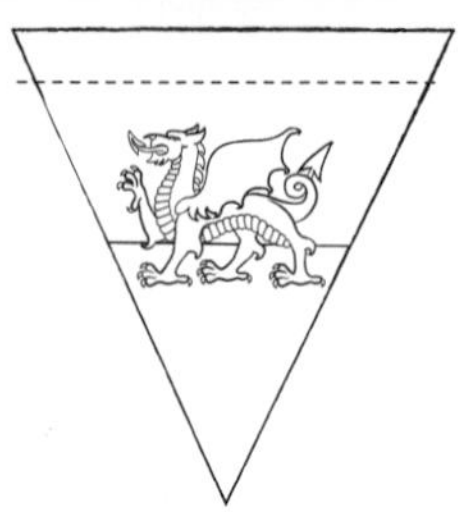

Why not decorate your desk with Great British mini bunting? Here's how.

You will need

- a pencil
- 10 pieces of paper
- colouring pencils
- scissors
- a stapler
- ribbon.

1. Use a pencil to trace the flags opposite as many times as you can onto your pieces of paper.

2. Colour in your flags and cut them out.

3. Fold the flag along the dotted line and staple them to the ribbon so they are 5 cm apart.

4. String up your bunting.

HOLIDAY DRINKS

When the weather is warm, all you need is a long cool drink. Try these recipes for hot summer days.

Easy-peasy lemon fizz

You will need

- 5 lemons
- 120 g caster sugar
- sparkling water.

1. Carefully cut each lemon in half and squeeze as much juice as you can from each piece into a large jug.

2. Measure out the caster sugar and tip it into the jug as well.

3. Stir with a long-handled spoon until there are no sugar granules left at the bottom.

4. Top up the jug with sparkling water and enjoy on a hot day!

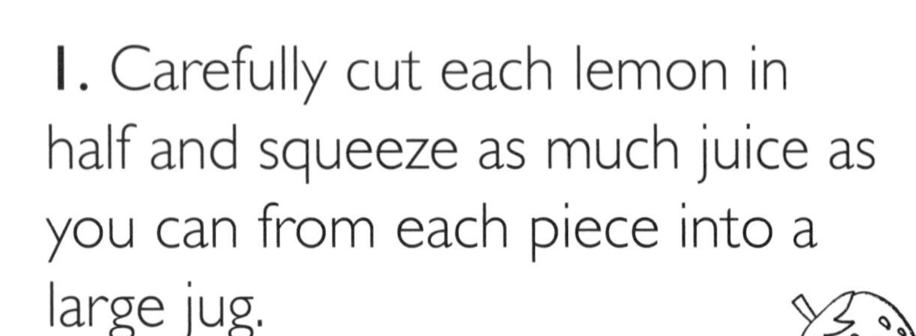

Brilliant berry smoothie

You will need

- 100 g strawberries
- 100 g raspberries
- a banana
- 100 g plain yogurt
- 100 g ice.

1. Remove the stems from all the strawberries. Cut them in half and place in a blending jug.

2. Slice the banana, and add to the jug, along with the raspberries.

3. Tip in the yogurt, add the ice and blend until smooth. Make sure that the blender you're using will crush ice. If not, just chill your smoothie before drinking it. Delicious!

Warning! *For this recipe, you'll need a blender. Make sure you ask an adult to help you.*

E R

GREAT BRITISH DEFENDERS

This castle needs defending! Finish drawing the army to keep invaders out. Don't forget to place your army in good defending positions.

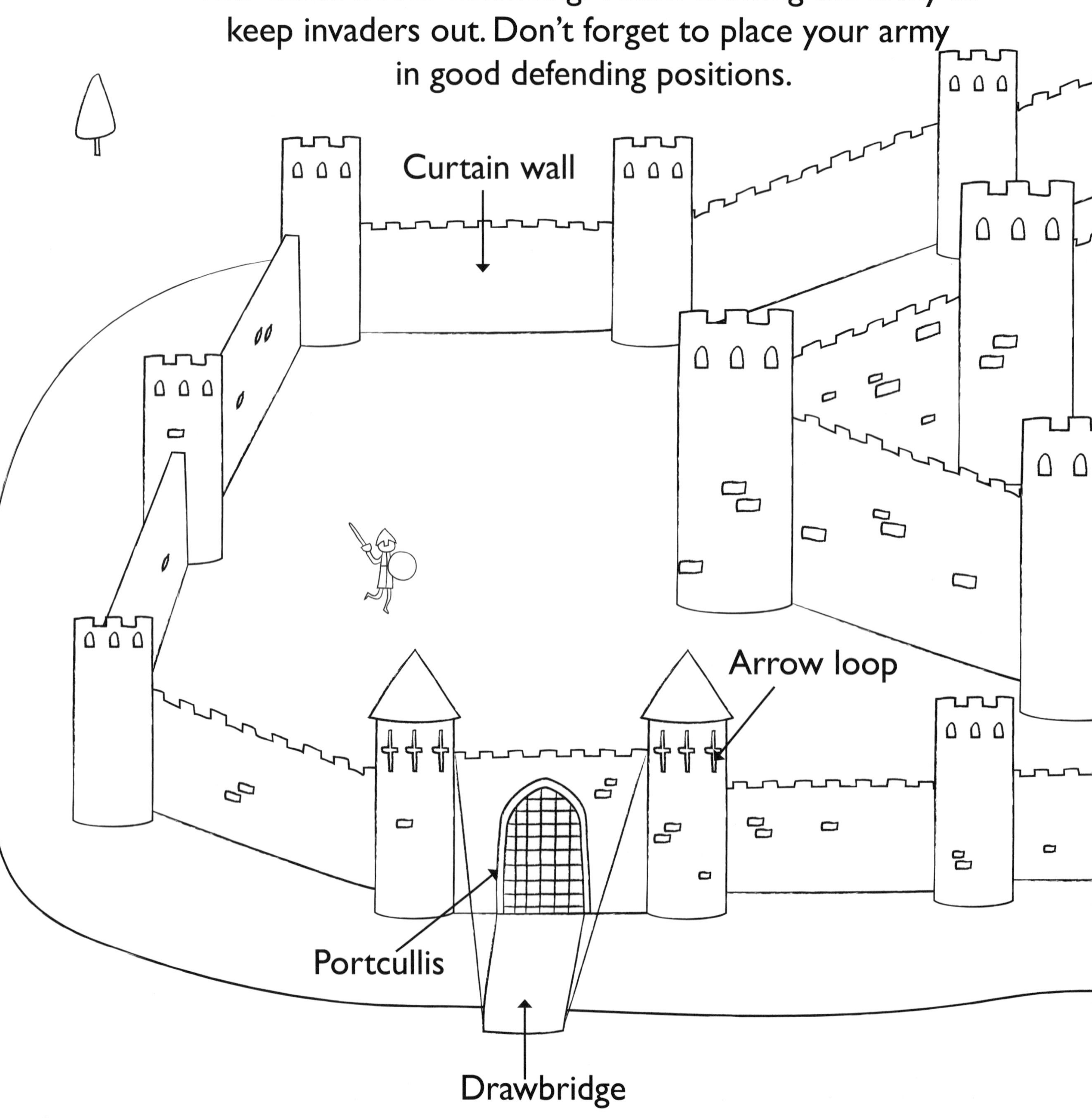

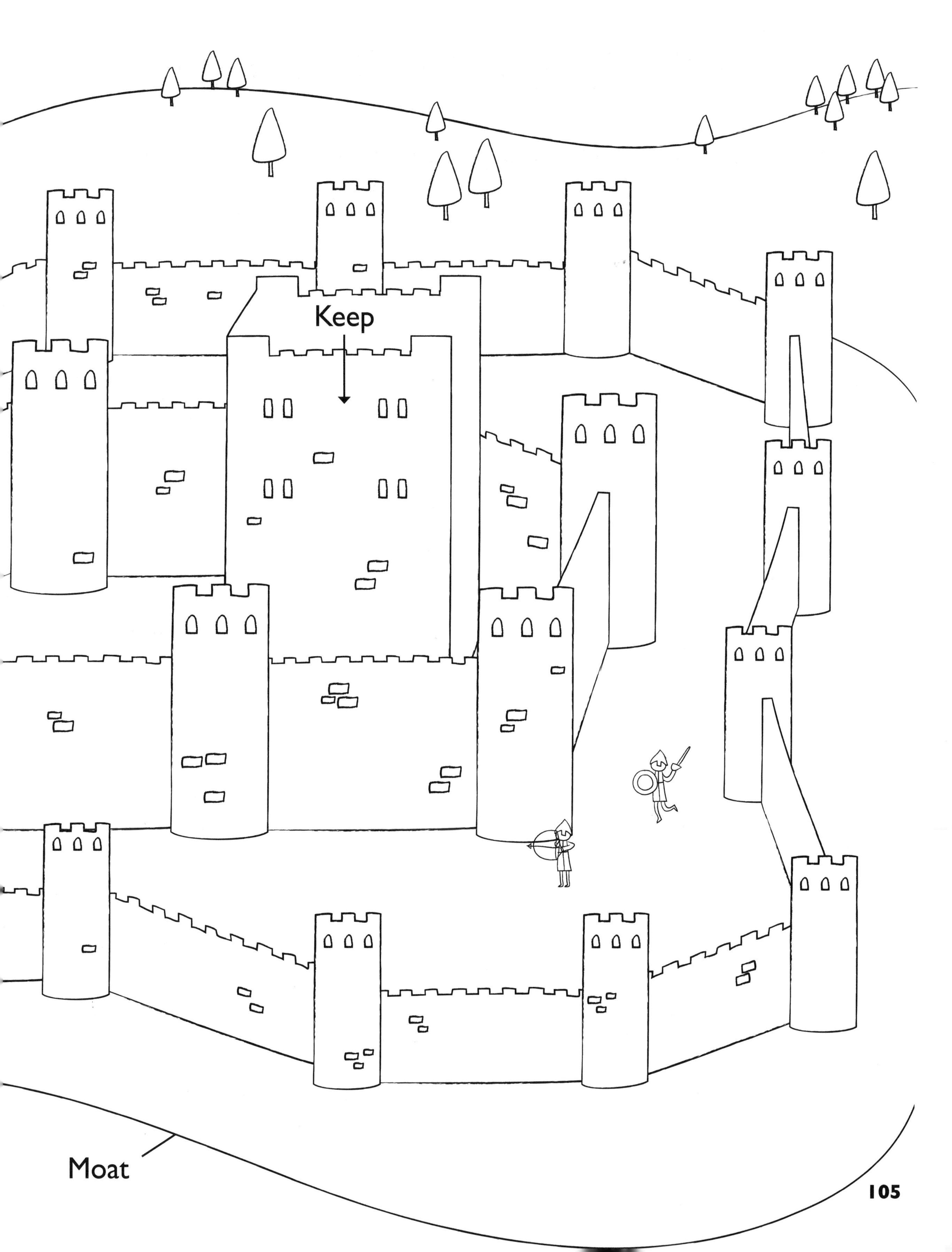
Keep
Moat

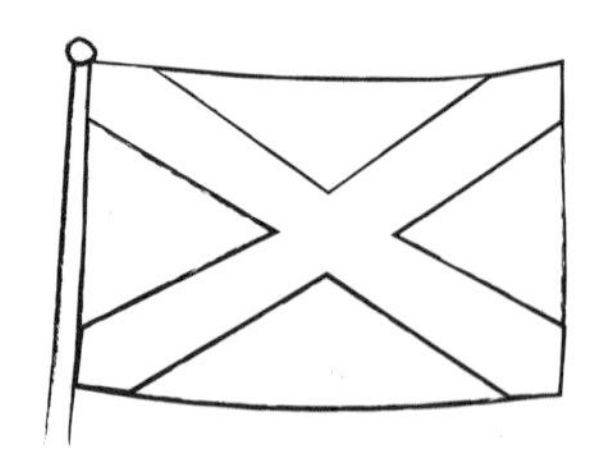

I-SPY SCOTLAND

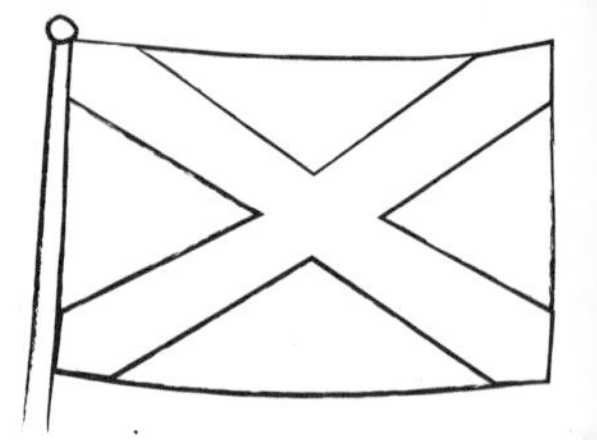

Put a tick next to each of the things below that you see when you are out and about in Scotland.

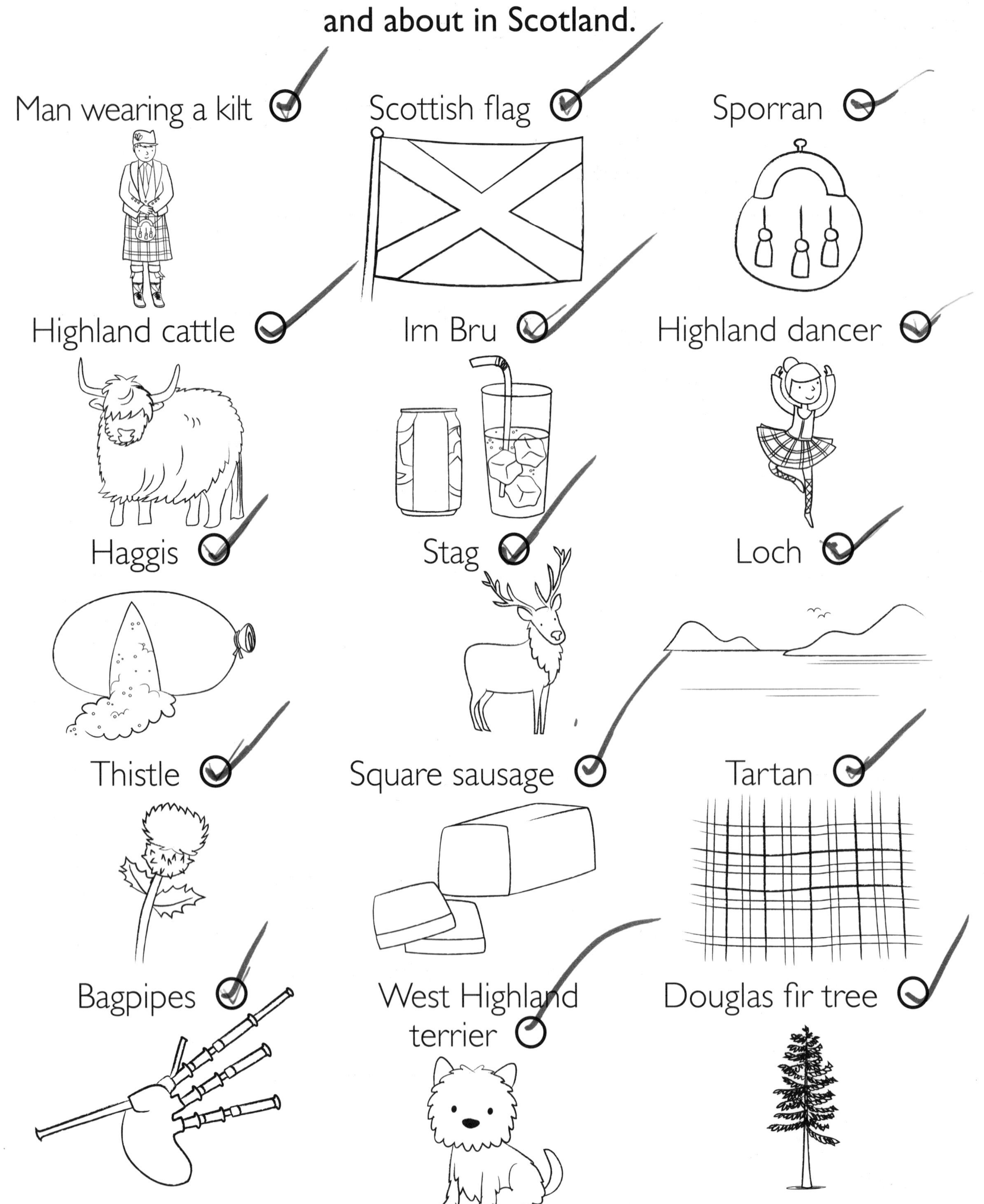

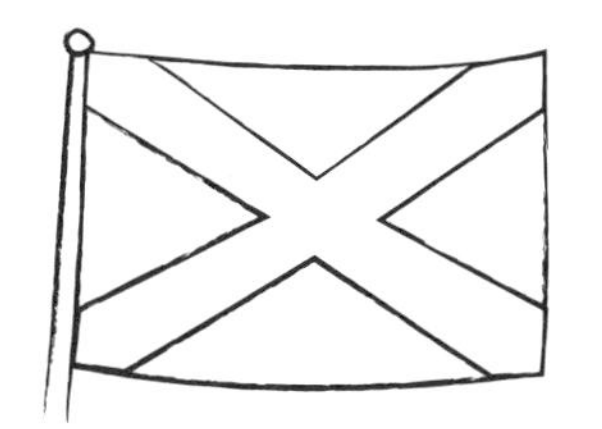

SCOTTISH MACAROONS

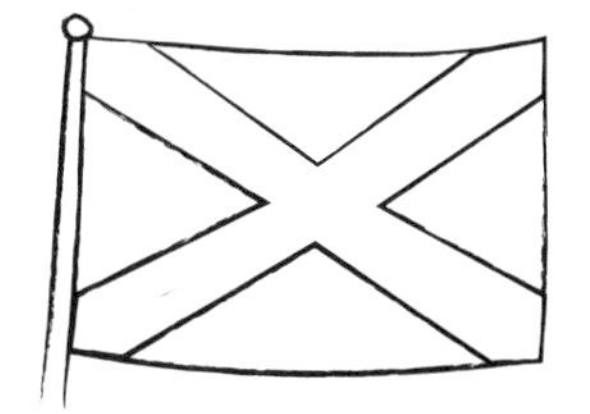

Make these and you will never look at a spud in the same way.

Ingredients

- 100 g potatoes
- 2 tbsp butter
- 1 tbsp milk
- 3 drops vanilla essence
- 500 g icing sugar
- 100 g desiccated coconut
- 300 g dark chocolate, in pieces.

Equipment

- Potato peeler
- table knife
- 2 saucepans
- colander
- 20 x 20 cm square cake tin
- large baking tray
- greaseproof paper
- 2 bowls – 1 small, 1 large
- sieve
- wooden spoon
- greaseproof paper
- a large plate.

Warning! *Make sure you ask an adult to help you whenever you'd like to use the hob.*

1. Carefully remove the skin of the potatoes with a peeler. Chop them in half with a table knife.

2. Put the potatoes into a saucepan and cover with water. Ask an adult to bring them to the boil, then simmer for 15–20 minutes until the potatoes are soft all the way through.

3. Drain the potatoes in a colander, then return to the pan and add the butter and milk, and mash until they are smooth with no lumps. Leave to cool.

4. Line a 20 x 20 cm cake tin and a baking tray with greaseproof paper.

5. Put the mashed potato and vanilla essence into a large bowl. Sieve roughly one third of the icing sugar into the mixture. Stir until all the sugar is mixed in. Add another third and stir again. Add the rest of the icing sugar until you have a sticky paste.

6. Spoon the mix into the cake tin and spread into the corners. Put it into the freezer for 2 hours.

7. Ask an adult to heat the oven to 160°C/gas mark 3.

8. Sprinkle the coconut onto the baking tray. Ask an adult to put it into the oven for 3–4 minutes or until golden and leave to cool.

9. Ask an adult to bring a pan of water to the boil. Remove from the heat. Put the chocolate into a bowl and place the bowl on top of the pan. Leave it to stand for 5 minutes. Stir the chocolate to check it's all melted.

10. Take the potato mix out of the freezer and cut it into small bars using a table knife.

11. Ask an adult to help you dip each bar into the melted chocolate and then roll it in the coconut.

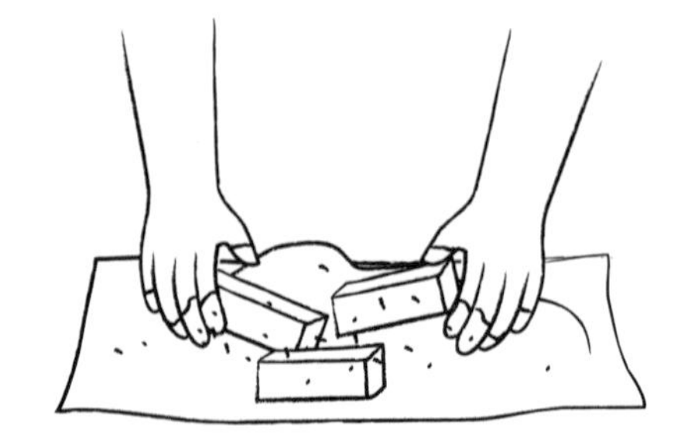

12. Place the bars onto a plate covered in greaseproof paper, and put them in the fridge to set.

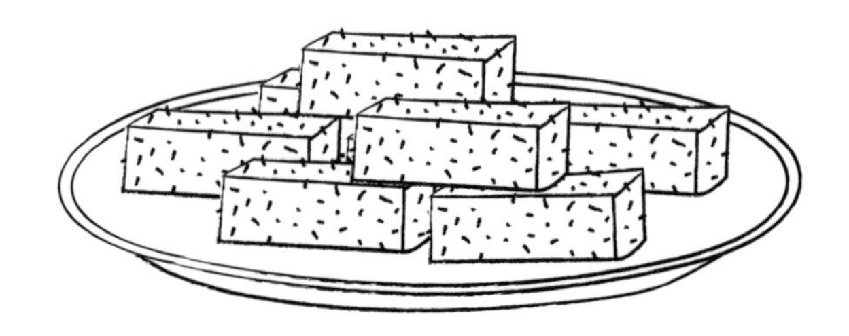

Legend has it that a monster lives in Loch Ness – draw your own monster here!

CRAZY GOLF

Did you know golf was invented in Scotland?
Create your own course and play a game of mini golf today.

You will need

- colouring pencils
- scissors
- glue
- table-tennis ball
- walking stick or hockey stick.

1. Colour in the shape opposite using any colours that you like. This is called the 'arch'.

2. Carefully cut out the shape.

3. Fold along all of the dotted lines to form the arch.

4. Apply glue to the tabs and then stick your arch together. Leave it to dry.

How to play the game

1. Place your finished arch on the floor and then put a table-tennis ball opposite the hole, around a metre away.

2. The first player must tap the table-tennis ball gently with the walking stick or hockey stick and attempt to get it through the hole. If he/she doesn't manage to get the ball through the hole first time ask him/her to try again.

3. The winner is the player who gets the ball through the hole in the fewest number of tries.

Great British tip
When you've tackled this course, get creative by moving the arch further away, putting it on a ramp of books or adding obstacles.

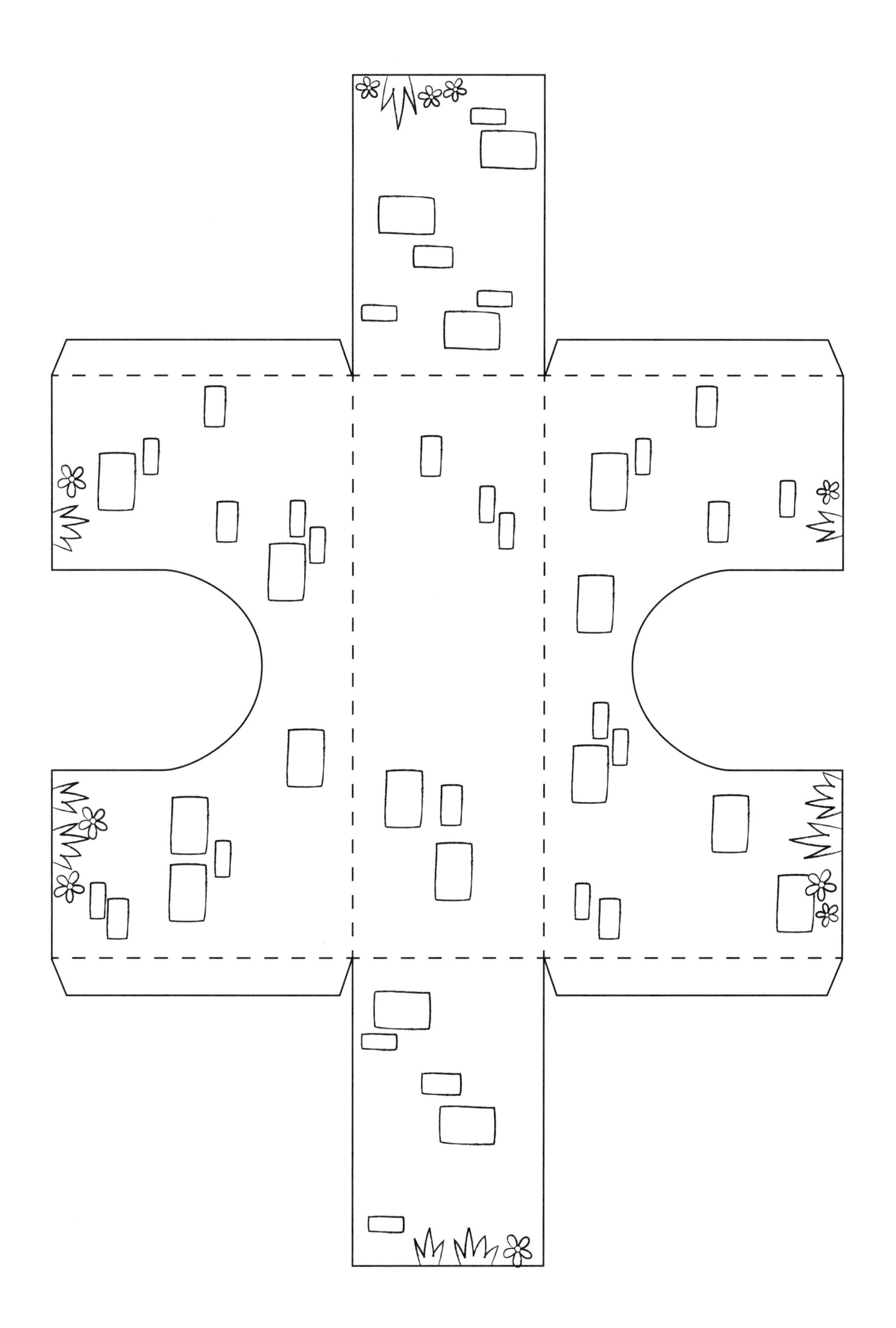

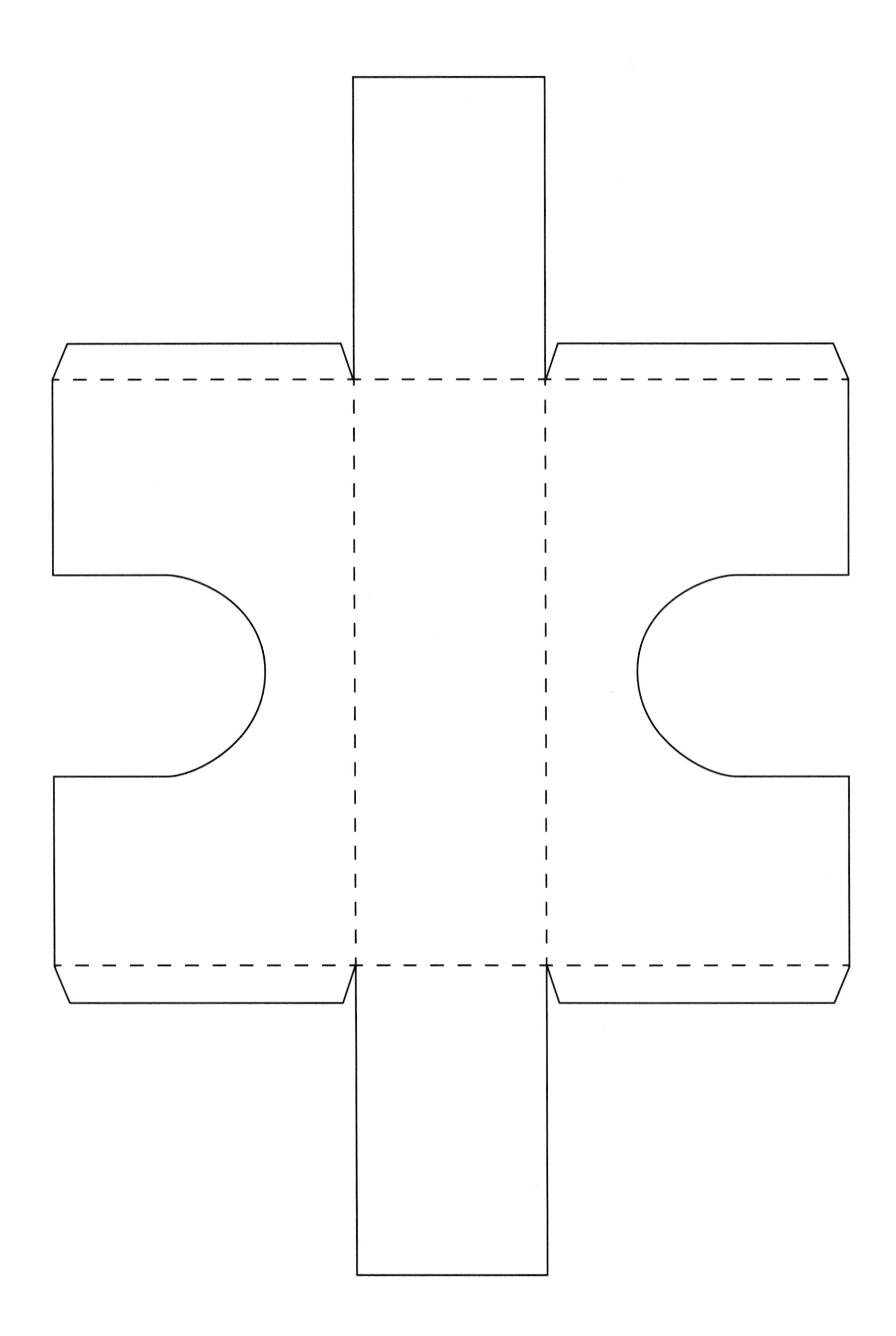

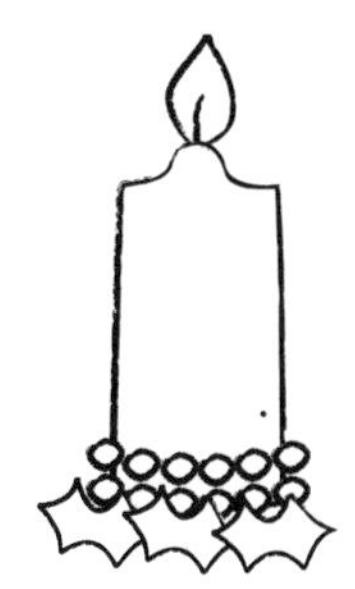

SCOTTISH SHORTBREAD

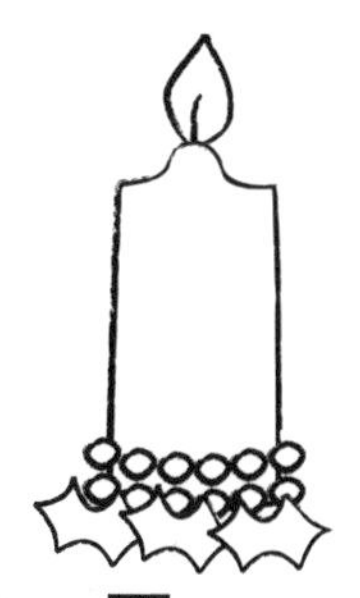

It wouldn't be Christmas without some homemade treats. Try making this Scottish shortbread for everyone with a sweet tooth!

You will need

- greaseproof paper
- 350 g plain flour
- 100 g caster sugar
- pinch of salt
- 225 g butter.

1. Ask an adult to preheat the oven to 170°C/gas mark 4.

2. Grease a baking tray with butter and line with greaseproof paper.

3. Sift the flour into a large bowl. Add the sugar, a pinch of salt and mix together.

4. Rub in the butter until the mixture is like breadcrumbs.

Warning! *Make sure you ask an adult to help you whenever you'd like to use the oven.*

5. Knead the mixture well until it holds together, then gently roll it into a square, about 25 x 25 cm and 2-3 cm thick.

6. Carefully mark out slices with a knife and decorate by pricking with a fork.

7. Bake in the oven for 30-40 minutes, or until golden-brown.

8. Ask an adult to help you remove it from the oven. Leave to cool on a wire rack and dust with caster sugar.

Handy hint: Put your shortbread in a pretty box to make the perfect gift.

What has the fisherman caught in his net?

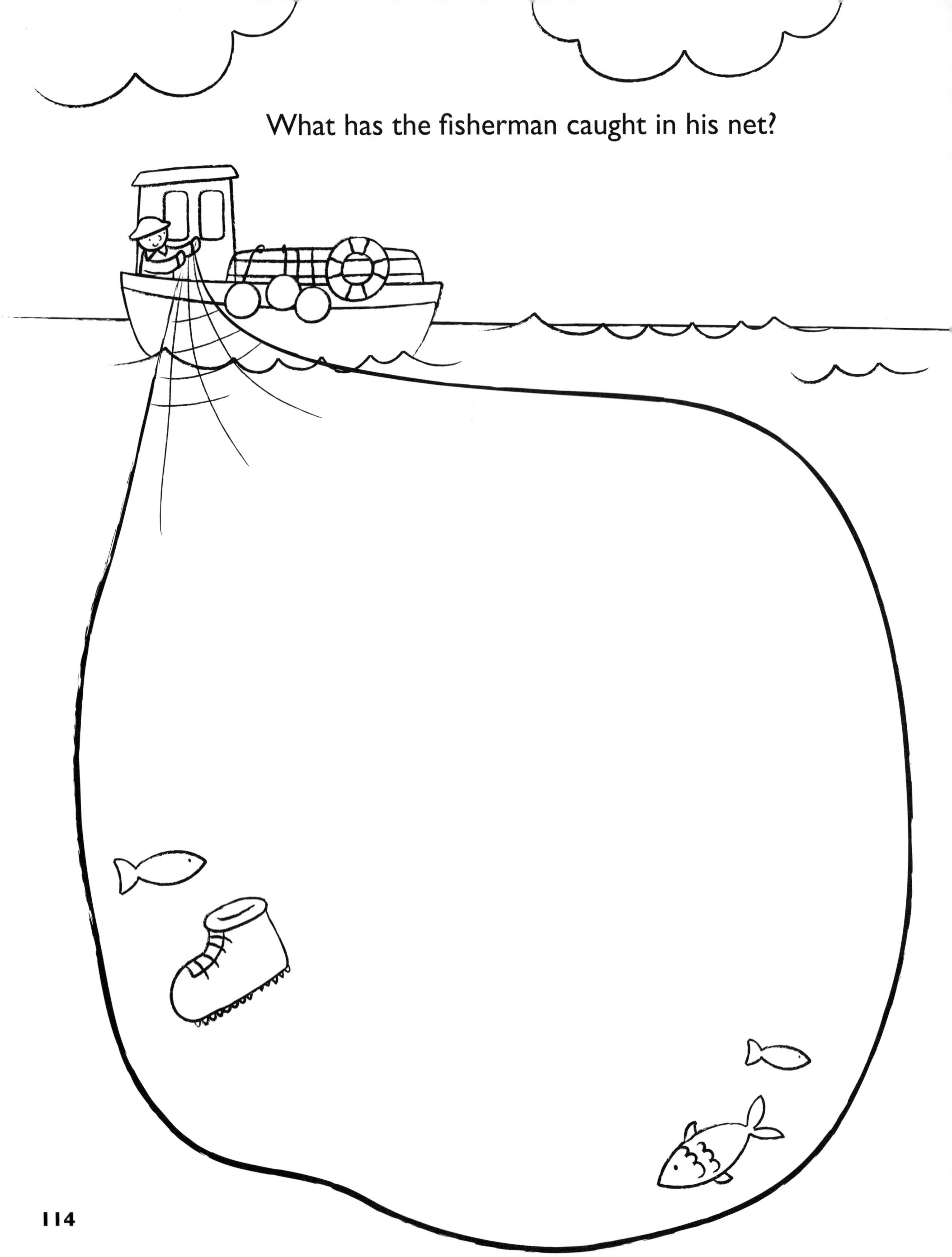

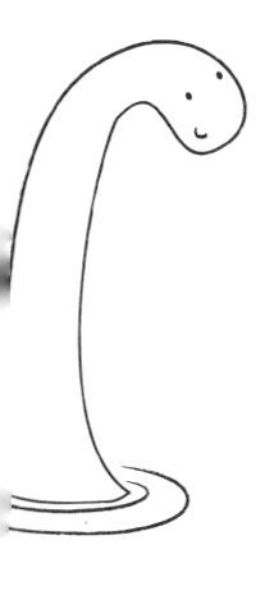

LOCH NESS MONSTER

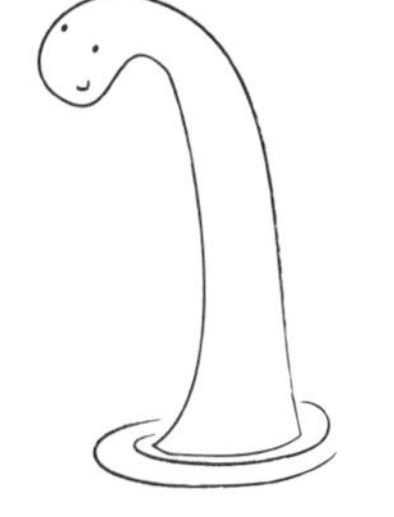

Celebrate St Andrew's Day, on November 30th, by sculpting Scotland's most mysterious resident – the Loch Ness Monster.

You will need

- self-hardening clay
- table knife
- paint
- paintbrush
- PVA glue
- pair of googly eyes.

1. Take a tennis-ball-sized lump of self-hardening clay and roll it into a sausage shape about 40 cm long.

2. Use a table knife to cut the clay into four equal pieces.

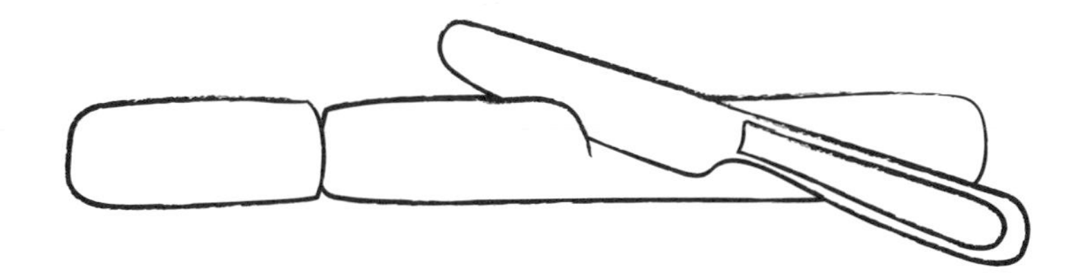

3. Take two of the pieces of clay and bend them into arch shapes. The clay may need to be rolled a little more if it's not long enough.

4. Roll one of the straight pieces into a point and bend it over slightly to make a tail. Take the other piece and bend it over 3 cm to make Nessie's head and neck.

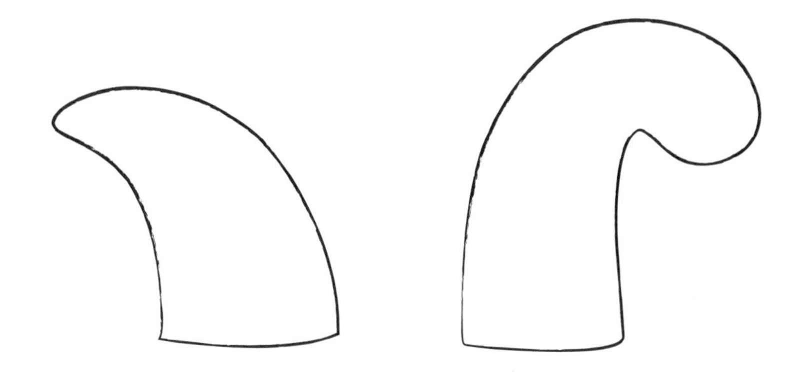

5. Leave your pieces to dry following the directions on the packet of clay.

6. When your clay is dry, paint it. There have never been any official sightings of Nessie so you can paint yours any colour you like. Why not try the colours of the Scottish flag, blue and white? Leave it to dry.

7. To make your Nessie nice and shiny, paint a coat of PVA glue over each piece and leave to dry.

Great British fact

Loch Ness is big! There is more water in Scotland's Loch Ness than there is in all of the other lakes in Great Britain put together. No wonder Nessie is so hard to find!

8. Glue the googly eyes on either side of Nessie's head. Leave it to dry. Now you can say you've seen the Loch Ness Monster.

I-SPY WALES

Put a tick next to each of the things below that you spy when you are out and about in Wales.

WELSH CAKES

These are a delicious tea-time treat, traditionally called 'pice ar y maen' in Welsh.

Ingredients

- 225 g plain flour, plus extra for dusting
- 85 g caster sugar
- 1 tsp mixed spice
- 1 tsp baking powder
- ¼ tsp salt
- 105 g butter, cut into cubes
- 50 g currants
- 1 egg, beaten
- a little milk.

Equipment

- Table knife, to cube the butter
- 2 bowls – 1 small, 1 large
- fork, to beat the egg
- rolling pin
- 7 cm circular cutter
- frying pan
- fish slice
- kitchen paper.

1. Put the flour, sugar, spice, baking powder, salt and 100 g of your butter into a large bowl.

Warning! *Make sure you ask an adult to help you whenever you'd like to use the hob.*

2. Use your fingertips to rub the butter into the dry ingredients. Keep rubbing until all the big lumps have gone and your bowl looks like it is full of crumbs.

3. Add the currants and stir in the beaten egg until you get a stiff dough that you can squash together with your hands. If your mix looks too crumbly, add a little milk. If it's a bit sticky, add some more flour.

4. Sprinkle some flour onto your work surface and rolling pin and roll out your dough until it is 1.5 cm thick. Add a splash more milk if your dough starts to dry out too much.

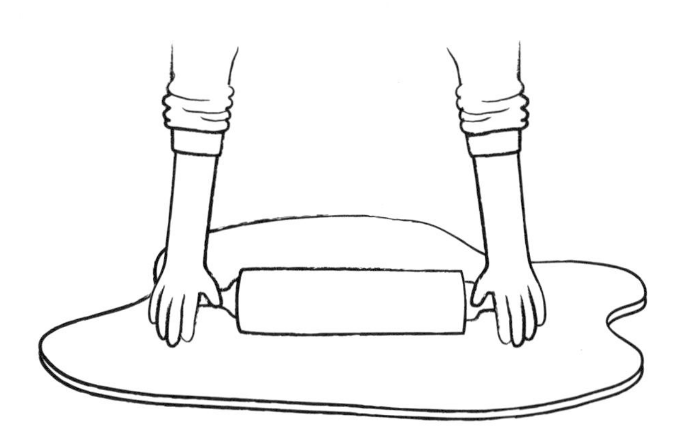

5. Use a 7 cm circular cutter to cut circles out of your dough. Squash together any leftover dough and roll it out again. Cut as many circles as you can so there's no wasted dough.

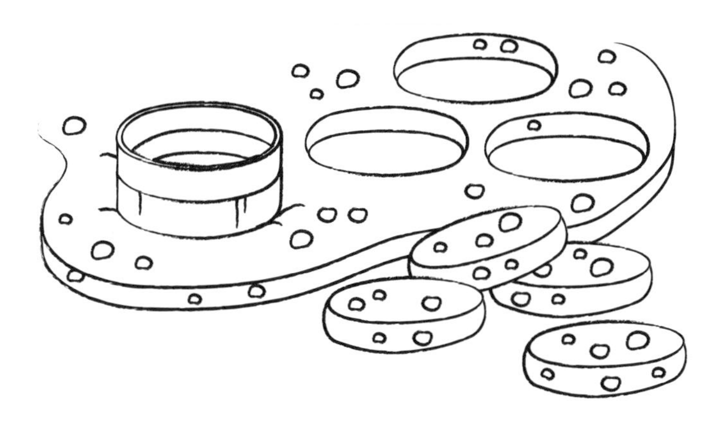

6. Ask an adult to melt the rest of your butter (5 g) in a frying pan over a low heat.

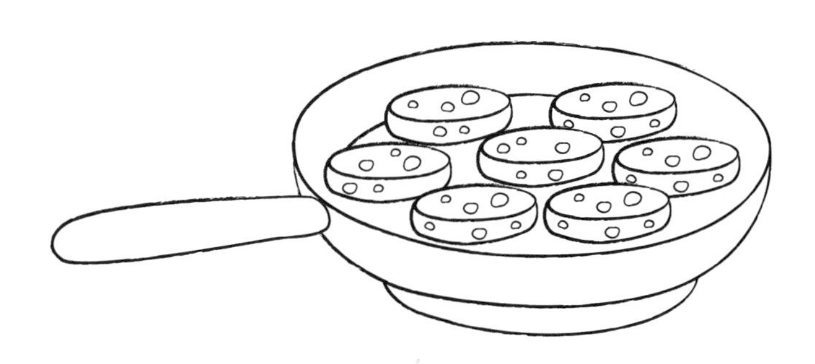

7. Ask an adult to add your cakes to the pan and fry for 3–4 minutes on each side. Carefully scoop them out with a fish slice and leave them to cool on kitchen paper.

8. Serve your cakes with butter and lots of yummy jam!

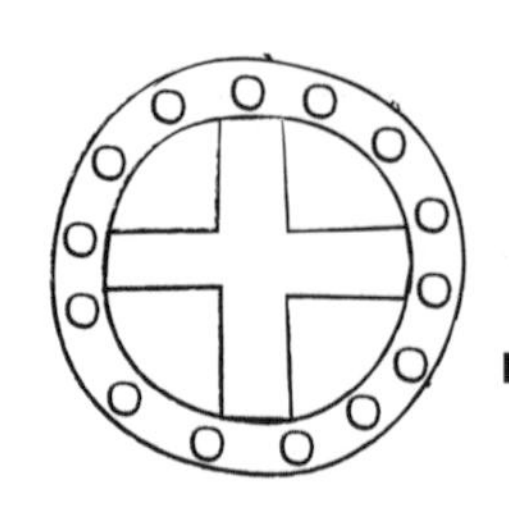

THE KNIGHTS OF THE ROUND TABLE

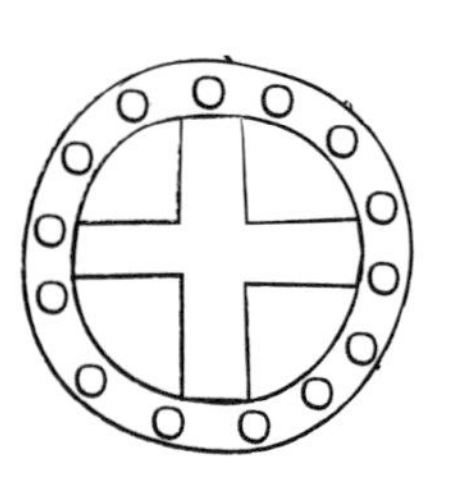

Only the bravest knights were invited to sit at King Arthur's Round Table. Make your own shield so you can join them.

You will need

- large cardboard box
- a pencil
- scissors
- newspaper
- paints
- paintbrush
- ruler
- masking tape.

1. Use your pencil to draw a large shield shape on the side of your cardboard box. Cut it out.

2. Lay your shield on newspaper and paint it any way you like. How about a fierce dragon or lion on the front to scare your opponent? Paint the back. Leave to dry.

3. To make an arm loop for your shield: cut a strip of cardboard measuring 10 cm x 30 cm.

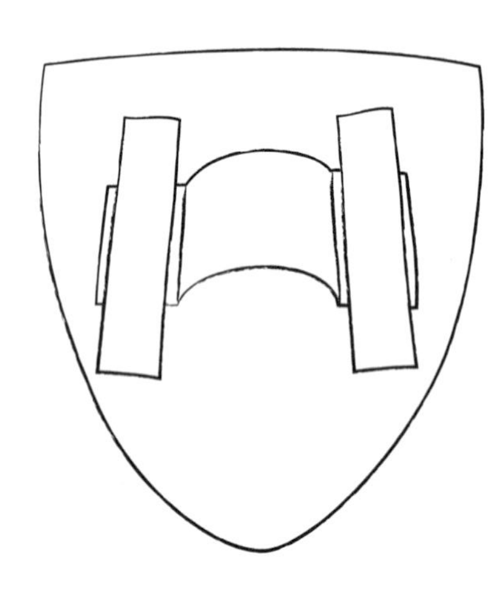

4. Bend your cardboard in a loop, like the diagram above, and stick the sides to the back of your shield using masking tape.

5. Put on your shield and get ready to face your foe in battle.

WHICH KNIGHT IS RIGHT?

Can you find the famous knight Sir Gawain from the clues below?

1. Sir Gawain's shield doesn't have a cross on it
2. He has a round shield with lions on it
3. He has a pointy helmet
4. His visor is up.

Can you also find two identical knights?

CORNISH SAFFRON BUNS

Saffron can be very expensive, but you only need to use a little pinch to make these yummy yellow buns.

Ingredients

- Pinch of saffron
- 1 tbsp hot water
- 600 g white bread flour, plus extra for dusting
- pinch of salt
- 125 g butter, cut into cubes, plus extra for greasing
- 7 g sachet of fast-action yeast
- 80 g caster sugar
- 1 egg, beaten
- 150 ml milk
- 100 ml water
- 175 g currants.

Equipment

- Table knife, to cube the butter
- 3 bowls – 1 small, 2 large
- fork, to beat the egg
- egg cup
- 2 large baking trays
- kitchen paper
- wooden spoon
- cling film
- wire rack.

Warning! *Make sure you ask an adult to help you whenever you'd like to use the hob or oven.*

1. Put the saffron in an egg cup and ask an adult to add the hot water. Leave to stand for 15 minutes.

2. Use kitchen paper to grease two large baking trays with butter.

3. Mix the flour and salt together in a large bowl. Add the cubed butter and use your fingertips to rub it in until your bowl looks like it is filled with crumbs.

4. Add the yeast, sugar and saffron water and mix well.

5. Pour the milk into a saucepan and ask an adult to slowly warm it on the hob.

6. In another large bowl, mix the beaten egg, warm milk and water and then pour it into the flour mixture. Stir together until you have a sticky dough.

7. Sprinkle the spare flour onto your surface and knead the dough for 5 minutes until it is stretchy and smooth.

8. Add the currants and squash them into the dough until they are all mixed in.

9. Break your dough into 12 and shape each piece into a ball.

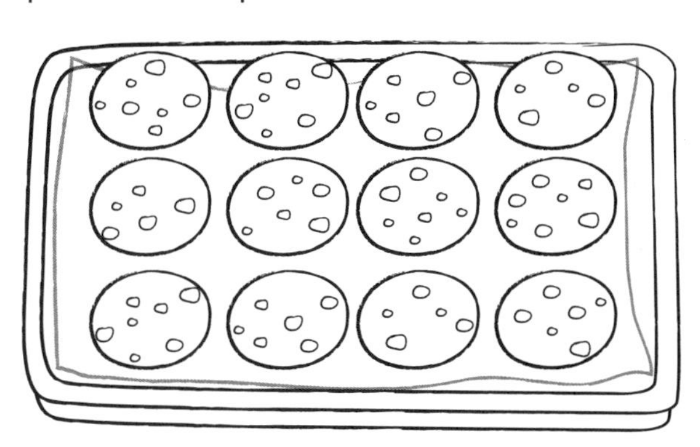

10. Place the balls onto the baking trays, 5 cm apart, and cover loosely with cling film.

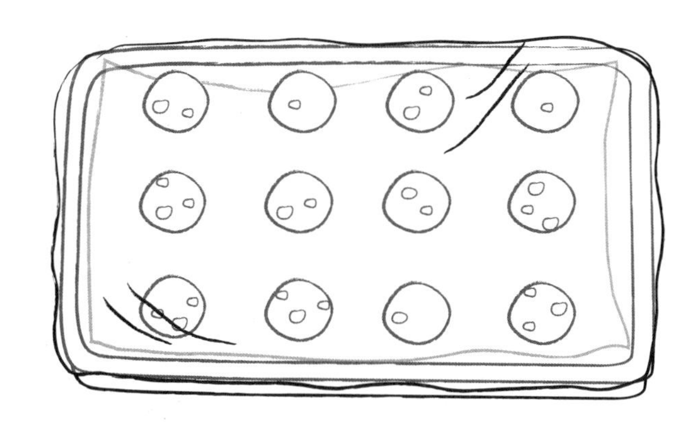

11. Leave in a warm place for 45 minutes. They should have doubled in size.

12. Ask an adult to preheat the oven to 220°C/gas mark 7.

13. Ask an adult to put your buns into the oven for 20 minutes and then leave them to cool on a wire rack.

POST A NOTE

Colour these postcards, then write a message home from each place.

To

Scotland

To

Wales

To

England

SPOOKY SPOTS

Can you find ten Halloween pumpkins hidden in this scene?

STICKY TOFFEE PUDDING

This gooey dessert is perfect to warm you up on a cold winter day.

Ingredients

- 175 g dates, chopped
- 1 tsp baking soda
- 300 ml boiling water
- 195 g butter, room temperature, plus extra for greasing
- 170 g caster sugar
- 2 eggs, beaten
- 225 g plain flour
- 1 tsp baking powder
- 1 tsp vanilla essence
- 270 g soft brown sugar
- 300 ml double cream.

Equipment

- Table knife, to chop the dates
- 2 bowls – 1 small, 1 large
- fork, to beat the eggs
- ovenproof dish
- kitchen paper
- wooden spoon
- saucepan
- jug.

Warning! *Make sure you ask an adult to help you whenever you'd like to use the hob or the oven.*

1. Put the dates and baking soda into a bowl. Ask an adult to pour over the boiling water. Soak for 1 hour.

2. Ask an adult to preheat the oven to 200°C/gas mark 6.

3. Use kitchen paper to grease your ovenproof dish with butter.

4. Put 70 g of butter, all of the caster sugar, beaten eggs, flour, baking powder and vanilla essence into a bowl. Mix them together until you have a sloppy mixture. Stir in the dates and any leftover soaking water.

5. Spoon the mixture into the ovenproof dish. Ask an adult to put it into the oven for 40 minutes. Leave it to cool for 10 minutes.

6. For the sauce, put the remaining butter (125 g), brown sugar and double cream into a saucepan and ask an adult to bring it to the boil for 3 minutes.

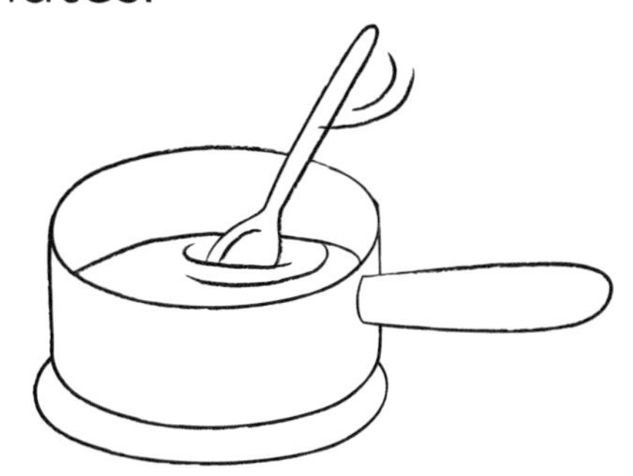

7. Pour the sauce into a jug and serve with the pudding.

Great British tip

You can also serve your pudding with a dollop of vanilla ice cream for a bit of extra luxury.

Three young bakers have entered their creations into the village show. Can you work out who got first, second and third place?

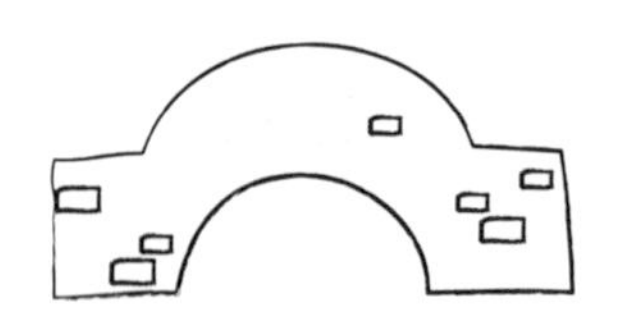

POOH STICKS

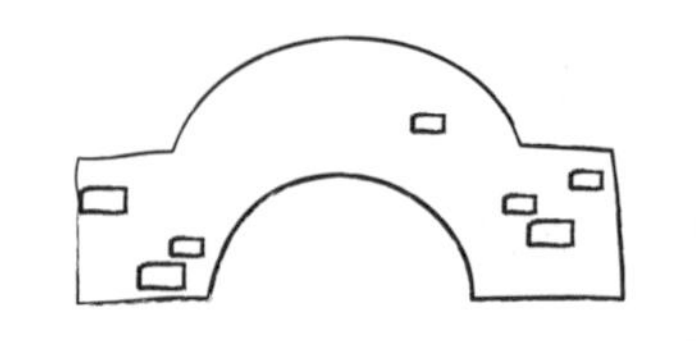

The game of pooh sticks is a Great British tradition. There's even a World Pooh Sticks Championships, held each year in Oxfordshire.

You will need

- a stick each
- a footbridge
- a stream.

1. Ask each player to find a stick and meet you on the footbridge.

2. Stand in the middle of the bridge and hold your sticks over the upstream side.

3. One player says 'Pooh', and everyone must drop, not throw, their sticks into the water.

4. Go to the other side of the bridge and wait for the sticks to appear.

5. The winner is the player whose stick is the first to come out from beneath the bridge.

Great British rule

Only use natural sticks. Any lollipop or plastic sticks thrown into the stream counts as littering and leads to instant disqualification!

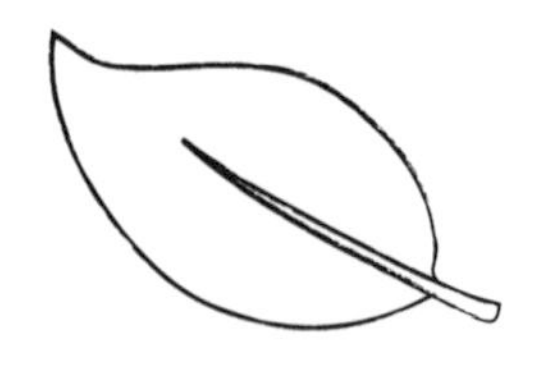

AUTUMN-LEAF GIFT BOX

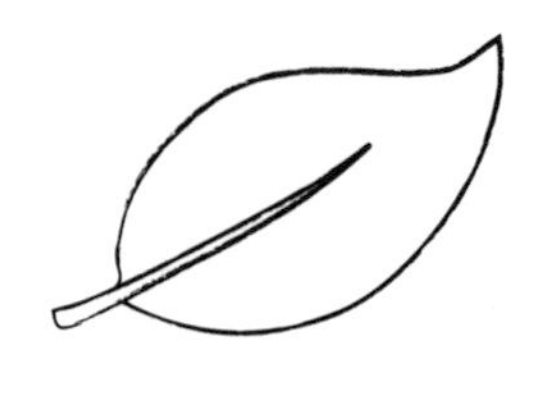

Give a chocolate conker to a friend in this gorgeous autumn-leaf gift box.

You will need

- Colouring pencils
- scissors
- chocolate conker.

1. Colour in the box template on the opposite page and then turn over the page and colour in the other side. This will be the inside of your box.

2. Cut out the coloured box template using a pair of scissors.

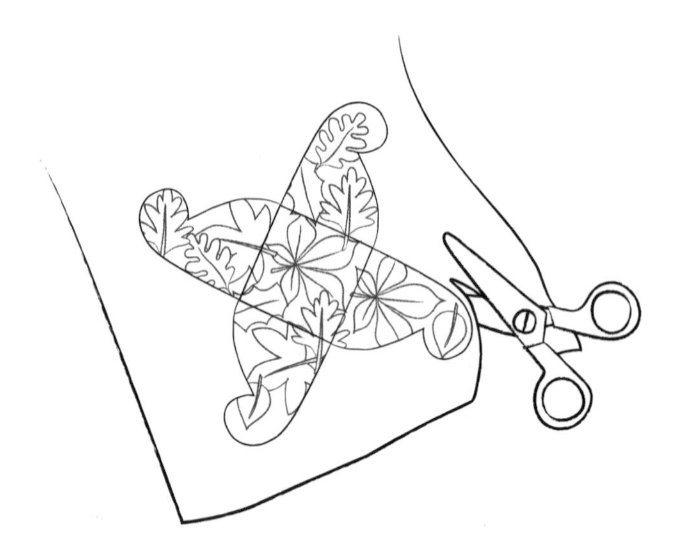

3. Fold the template along each of the dotted lines.

4. Place a chocolate conker in the centre of your box.

5. Take two opposite flaps and connect them together by folding them towards the centre and slotting them together.

6. Repeat step five with the other two opposite flaps, connecting them over the top of the first pair. Beautiful!

Great British tip

Want to give conkers to lots of friends? Simply trace the template rather than cut it out to make as many gift boxes as you like.

FAT RASCALS

These Yorkshire scones date back to Elizabethan times.

Ingredients

- 300 g self-raising flour, plus extra for dusting
- ½ tsp baking powder
- 130 g butter, cut into cubes
- 100 g caster sugar
- 1 tsp mixed spice
- 150 g mixed dried fruit
- zest of 1 orange, grated
- zest of 1 lemon, grated
- 50 ml double cream
- 2 eggs, beaten
- 50 g glacé cherries, halved
- 25 g flaked almonds.

Equipment

- Table knife, to cube the butter and halve the cherries
- 2 bowls – 1 small, 1 large
- fork, to beat the eggs
- grater, for the zests
- large baking tray
- greaseproof paper
- wooden spoon
- rolling pin
- pastry brush.

Warning! *Make sure you ask an adult to help you whenever you'd like to use the oven.*

1. Ask an adult to preheat the oven to 200°C/gas mark 6.

2. Take a large baking tray and line it with greaseproof paper.

3. Mix the flour and baking powder in a large bowl. Add the butter and use your fingertips to rub in the butter until your bowl looks like it is filled with crumbs.

4. Add the sugar, spice, dried fruit and zests, and stir together.

5. Add the cream and half of the egg mixture, and stir until you have a soft dough.

6. Dust your surface with flour and roll out the dough until it's 2.5 cm thick. Divide the dough into six pieces, shape into rounds and put them on the baking tray.

7. Brush each bun with the remaining egg. Press a cherry and almonds into the top of each bun.

8. Ask an adult to put them into the oven for 15 minutes until golden and then leave to cool.

9. Slice them in half and spread with clotted cream and strawberry jam. Yum!

CHOCOLATE CONKERS

What better way to celebrate autumn than with a heap of yummy chocolate conkers?

Ingredients

- 360 g smooth peanut butter
- 1 tsp vanilla essence
- 120 g butter, room temperature
- 400 g icing sugar, sifted
- 300 g dark chocolate, in pieces.

Equipment

- Sieve, for the icing sugar
- large baking tray
- greaseproof paper
- 2 bowls – 1 small, 1 large
- wooden spoon
- tablespoon
- saucepan
- fork.

1. Take a large baking tray and line it with greaseproof paper.

2. Mix the peanut butter, vanilla essence, butter and icing sugar in a bowl with a wooden spoon until it forms a thick dough.

Warning! *Make sure you ask an adult to help you whenever you'd like to use the hob.*

3. Scoop out conker-sized lumps of dough using a tablespoon. Shape the lumps of dough into balls by rolling them between your palms.

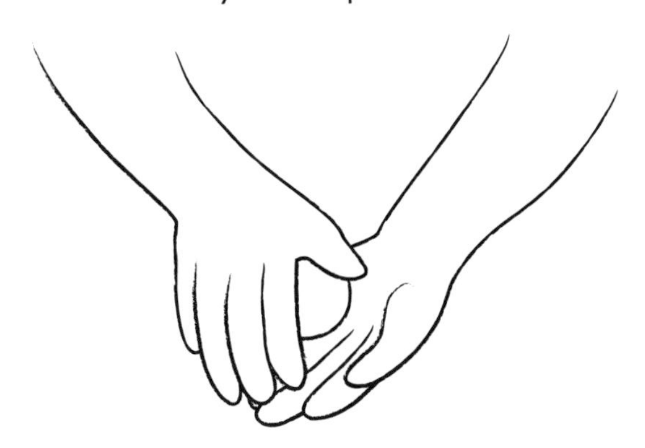

4. Lay each ball onto the baking tray, and put the sheet into the fridge to chill for 1 hour.

5. To melt the chocolate, ask an adult to bring a pan of water to the boil and then remove it from the heat.

6. Put your chocolate pieces into a small bowl and place the bowl on top of the pan. Leave it to stand for 5 minutes. Give the chocolate a stir to check that it has completely melted.

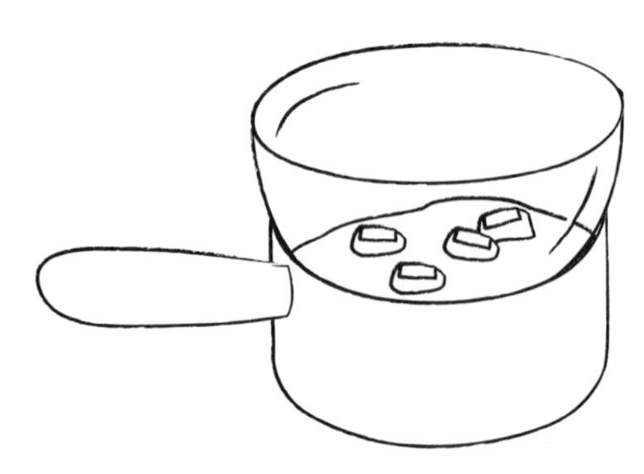

7. Push a fork into a peanut-butter ball and dip the ball into the chocolate. Leave a small circle of the peanut-butter dough showing.

8. Pull your fork out and put the chocolate-covered ball back onto your baking tray, chocolate-side down. Repeat for the rest of your peanut-butter balls. Put them back in the fridge for 20 minutes to set.

9. Pile your conkers up and enjoy with a glass of cold milk.

SAVE THE QUEEN!

Oh no! The Queen has got lost in the maze at her annual garden party. Can you help her find her way out and get back to the palace?

GET STICKING

Collect your favourite leaves and glue them in a pattern on this page, then colour the cool design opposite.

Try to find as many different types of leaf as you can, so you get lots of shapes.

You can cover up all the writing on this page too.

REMEMBER, REMEMBER, THE 5TH OF NOVEMBER

It can get cold standing around outside waiting to see the fireworks on bonfire night. Make sure you are warm enough with this bobble hat.

You will need

- pencil
- pair of compasses
- ruler
- 1 old thin knitted jumper
- 1 piece of paper
- felt-tip pen
- scissors
- 1 large needle
- thread
- thin card
- wool.

1. On a piece of paper carefully use a pair of compasses and a ruler to draw a hat shape that's 18 cm wide and 22 cm high at it's highest point. Cut out your template.

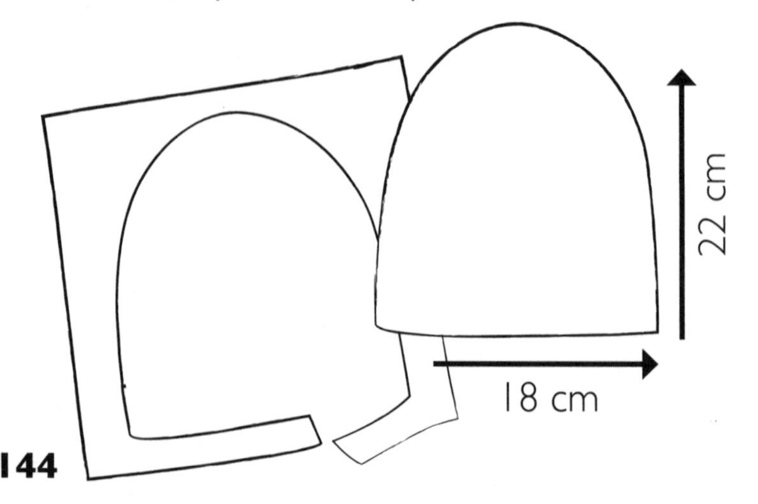

2. Place the template on the jumper so the flat edge of the template lies along the bottom of your jumper. Draw around it using a felt-tip pen. Repeat this so that you have two hat shapes on your jumper. Cut them out.

3. Place your hat shapes on top of one another, with the pattern on the inside.

4. Thread your needle and tie a knot in the end of the thread. Starting at the bottom left corner, 1.5 cm in from the cut edge of your hat shape, push the needle through the fabric and bring it back up and out the other side, roughly 1 cm from where you went in. Repeat this until you get to the bottom right corner, and tie a knot in the end of your thread. Leave the bottom edge open.

5. Turn your hat inside out so that your stitches are on the inside.

6. To make a pompom template, set your compasses to 3 cm and draw a circle on a piece of card. Then set them to 6 cm and draw another circle from the same centre point to make a doughnut shape. Do this twice.

8. Place one ring on top of the other and wrap the wool around the rings several times until you can no longer pass any any wool through the hole in the centre.

9. Trim the wool around the edge of the ring until you see the card inside. Carefully insert your scissors between the two pieces of card and cut all the way around the outside.

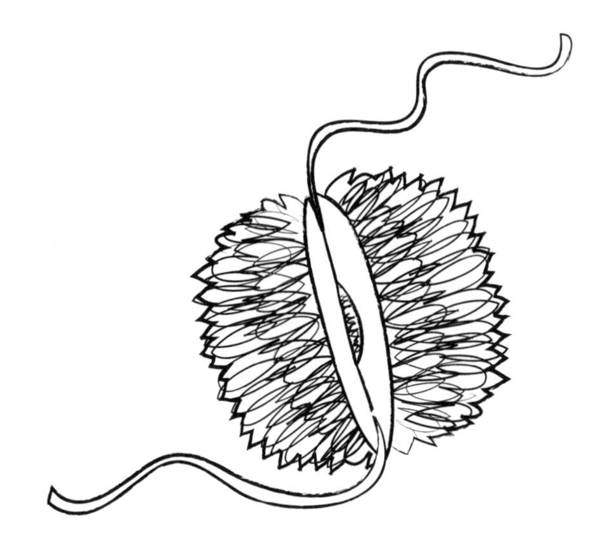

10. Push a piece of wool between the two pieces of card, wrap it around the centre twice and secure with a knot.

11. Pull away the card rings and fluff up your pompom. Secure it to the top of your hat using a few stitches.

Spend the day
at Windsor Castle.
There's so much to see!
Look out for ...
* 3 princesses laughing
* 2 very serious guards
* 1 corgi dog, running
round the castle yard
* 7 birds in a flap
* 1 visitor taking a snap

THEATRELAND!

This family are off to see a show in London's West End.
Can you help them get to the theatre in time?

WELCOME!

HOT SAMOSAS

These crispy vegetable samosas are a perfect snack and easy to make.

You will need

- 2 tbsp vegetable oil
- 1 medium onion, chopped
- 2 cm ginger, grated
- 1 tsp mustard seeds
- 100 g frozen peas
- 100 g frozen sweetcorn
- 1 tbsp ground coriander
- 1 tsp ground cumin
- 1 tsp mild chilli powder
- 1 tsp curry powder
- 1 large potato, boiled and cubed
- 1 tbsp lemon juice
- ½ tsp salt
- ½ pack filo pastry
- 50 g melted butter.

1. Ask an adult to preheat the oven to 220 °C/gas mark 7.

2. Ask an adult to help you heat the oil in a small frying pan. When the oil is hot, add the onion, ginger and mustard seeds, and cook until the onions are soft.

3. Add the peas and sweetcorn and give the pan a good stir.

Warning! *Make sure you ask an adult to help you whenever you'd like to use a sharp knife or the oven.*

4. In a bowl, mix the remaining spices and add them to the pan.
Stir well before adding the potato, lemon juice and salt. Cook for ten minutes. Leave to cool.

5. Unroll the pastry and cut in half lengthways. Peel off two strips and lay them on top of one another. Cover the rest with a damp tea towel to stop them drying out.

6. Put a tablespoonful of mixture on to one end of the pastry.

7. Take the corner of the pastry and fold it over the mixture.

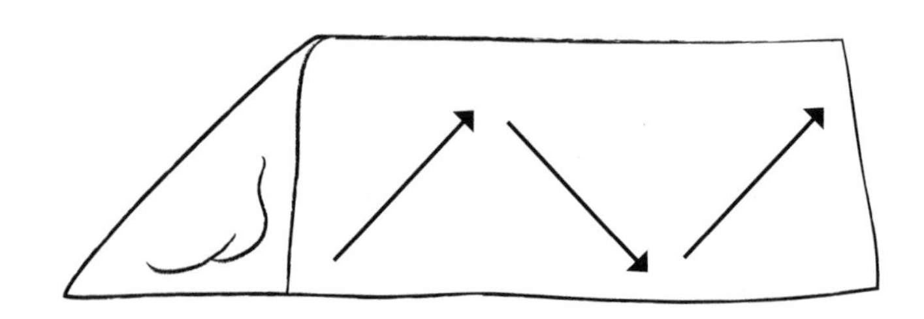

8. Keep folding the pastry over the mixture until you have a triangle-shaped parcel. Cut away any extra pastry. Repeat with the rest of the pastry until you've used all of your mixture.

9. Place your samosas on a greased baking tray and brush with melted butter. Ask an adult to put them in the oven for ten minutes or until golden brown.

10. Leave to cool before serving. They go perfectly with a good dollop of mango chutney.

Can you find the ingredients listed opposite in this wordsearch?

M	C	S	O	E	B	C	R	J	L	U	D	R
W	U	M	T	R	U	O	F	P	E	N	L	E
C	R	S	A	L	T	R	I	N	M	T	I	D
U	R	O	T	S	T	I	L	R	O	D	O	W
M	Y	W	O	A	E	A	O	O	N	S	E	O
I	P	L	P	E	R	N	P	C	J	I	L	P
N	O	I	N	O	G	D	A	T	U	T	B	I
E	W	R	G	F	H	E	S	E	I	T	A	L
L	D	C	B	Z	N	R	T	E	C	L	T	L
Q	E	U	S	A	E	P	R	W	E	I	E	I
C	R	F	I	A	O	L	Y	S	K	D	G	H
D	B	N	U	M	L	A	N	C	W	T	E	C
G	I	N	G	E	R	T	V	R	E	X	V	O

MICROWAVED STEAMED PUDDING

Traditional steamed puddings can take hours to boil on the stove. Try this quick recipe for a delicious alternative.

Ingredients

- 100 g butter, room temperature
- 100 g caster sugar
- 1 tsp vanilla essence
- 2 eggs, beaten
- 1 tbsp milk
- 100 g self-raising flour
- 3 tbsp your favourite jam.

Equipment

- 2 bowls – 1 small, 1 large
- fork, to beat the eggs
- jug
- wooden spoon
- microwaveable dish.

1. Mix the butter and sugar in a large bowl until light and fluffy.

2. Put the vanilla, egg and milk in a jug and stir. Pour the liquid a little at a time into the butter and sugar until you have a smooth mixture and then stir in the flour.

Warning! *Make sure you ask an adult to help you whenever you'd like to use the microwave.*

3. Put the jam into the bottom of a microwaveable dish and then pour the mixture over the top.

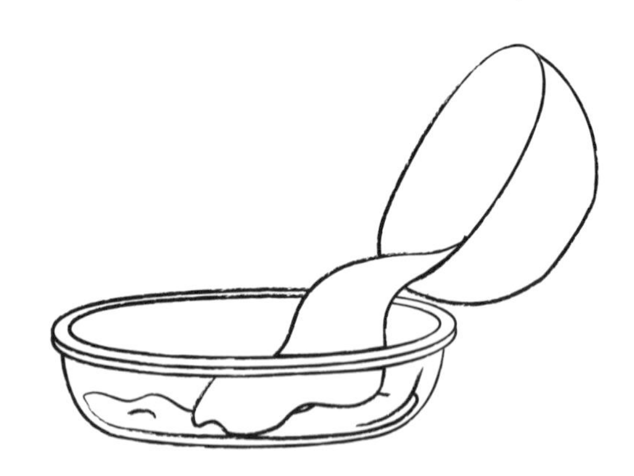

4. Ask an adult to cook in the microwave on high power for 4 minutes. Leave to stand for 2 minutes before serving. It goes best with lots of custard.

Great British tip

Swap the jam for syrup, lemon curd or fruit for different flavours.

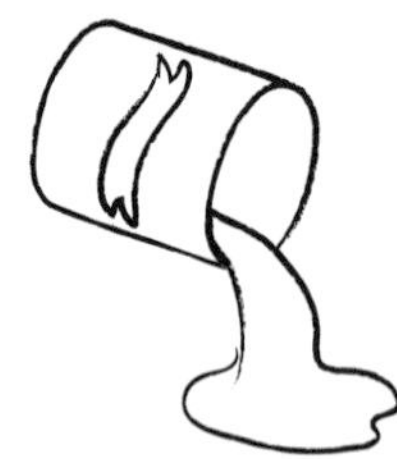

CHOCOLATE FUDGE

There are only four ingredients between you and lip-lickingly good fudge.

Ingredients
- 500 g chocolate, in pieces
- 60 g butter, cut into cubes
- 1 tsp vanilla essence
- 1 x 397 g can sweetened condensed milk

Equipment
- Table knife, to cube the butter
- 20 x 20 cm square cake tin
- tin foil
- scissors
- saucepan
- table knife.

1. Cover the inside of a 20 x 20 cm cake tin with foil.

2. Add the chocolate, butter and vanilla essence into a saucepan and pour in the condensed milk.

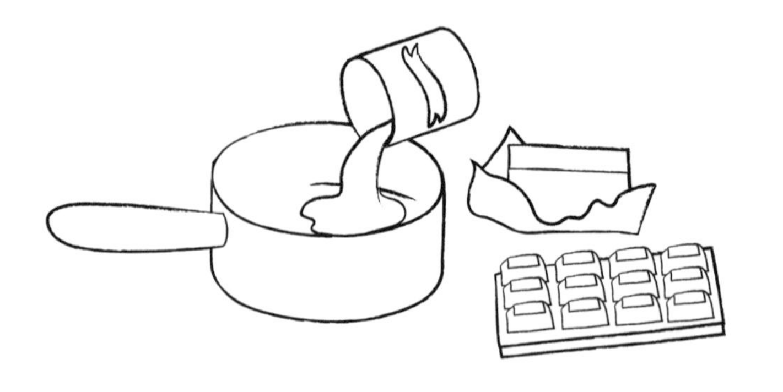

Warning! *Make sure you ask an adult to help you whenever you'd like to use the hob.*

3. Ask an adult to put the pan over a low heat until all of the chocolate is melted. Stir well.

4. Pour the mixture into the cake tin and leave to cool. When cool, place in the fridge and leave to set for 3 hours.

5. Remove from the fridge and cut into pieces with a table knife.

Great British tip
Take a pretty gift box, line it with tissue paper and pop in your fudge to make a sweet gift for a friend.

APPLE CRUMBLE

This British pudding is easy to make and the perfect way to round off a traditional Sunday lunch.

Warning! *Make sure you ask an adult to help you whenever you'd like to use the oven.*

Ingredients

- 100 g caster sugar
- 225 g butter, cut into cubes
- 210 g plain flour
- 450 g cooking apples, cut into 1.5 cm chunks
- 75 g soft brown sugar.

Equipment

- Table knife, to cut the butter and apples
- 2 large bowls
- wooden spoon
- large ovenproof dish.

1. Ask an adult to preheat the oven to 190°C/gas mark 5.

2. Put the caster sugar, butter and 200 g of flour into a large bowl. Rub the butter into the mixture, using your fingertips, until you have no big lumps of butter left and the mixture looks like breadcrumbs.

3. Put your chunks of apple into another bowl. Stir together with the brown sugar and 10 g of flour.

4. Tip your apple mix into a large ovenproof dish and cover evenly with your crumble topping from your first bowl.

5. Ask an adult to put the crumble into the oven for 1 hour until golden brown.

6. Leave to cool for 10 minutes before dishing up with lots of custard.

EIIR

BARA BRITH

This traditional Welsh recipe actually has tea inside the cake! Tea and cake in one mouthful, delicious.

Ingredients

- 225 g mixed dried fruit
- 400 ml strong, hot tea, no milk
- knob of butter
- 175 g self-raising flour
- 175 g wholemeal flour
- 1 tsp baking powder
- 1 ½ tsp mixed spice
- 60 g soft brown sugar
- 1 egg, beaten.

Equipment

- 3 bowls – 1 small, 2 large
- fork, to beat the egg
- teapot
- large loaf tin
- kitchen paper
- wooden spoon
- wire rack.

1. Put the dried fruit in a bowl and pour over the hot tea. Stir together and leave the fruit to soak overnight.

Warning! *Make sure you ask an adult to help you whenever you'd like to use the oven.*

2. Ask an adult to preheat the oven to 160°C/gas mark 3.

3. Use kitchen paper to grease the inside of a loaf tin with butter.

4. Tip both flours, the baking powder, spice and sugar into a large bowl and stir together.

5. Pour in the beaten egg and the fruit, along with any tea still in the bowl. Mix together until the fruit is evenly spread in the mixture.

6. Spoon your mixture into the loaf tin. Squash it into the corners and smooth on the top.

7. Ask an adult to put your cake in the oven for 1 hour and 20 minutes and then leave to cool for 10 minutes.

8. Remove your loaf from the tin and place on a wire rack to cool.

9. Cut up your loaf, spread the slices with butter and enjoy with more tea.

Complete the grid so that there is just one tea cup, flag, daffodil and piece of bara brith in each row, column and group of four squares.

WOODLAND MAZE

After a wintry walk in Batsford Arboretum, the Greens want to warm up with hot chocolates. Can you help them find their way to the café?

SOMERSET HOUSE
SKATERS

Get your skates on and spot the ten differences between these two pictures.

CHRISTMAS CRAFTS

If you're short of money this Christmas, try these penny-saving ideas.

Orange clove

You will need

- an orange
- cloves
- ribbon.

1. Push the cloves into the skin of the orange in a shape like a spiral or a heart, or cover all of the orange in as many cloves as you can.

2. Leave the orange in a cool, dark place to dry out, until it shrinks slightly.

3. Take a ribbon and tie it around the orange. Put the middle of the ribbon at the top of the orange, wrap it underneath, then cross it over and wrap back to the top. Tie in a bow or a loop to finish it off.

If you want a different scent, you can also try using a lemon.

Handy hint: if it's difficult to push cloves into the orange skin, make a small hole first with a pin.

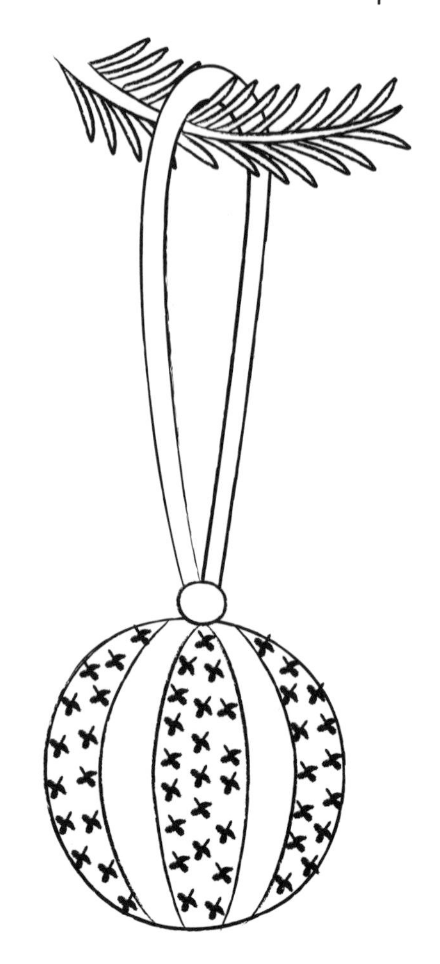

Christmas labels

You will need

- old Christmas cards
- scissors
- a pen
- a hole punch
- ribbon
- sticky tape.

1. Collect together last year's Christmas cards.

2. Cut out the picture from the front of the card. You can either cut around the image exactly, or just cut off part of the picture in a shape like a circle, square or rectangle.

3. Write the words 'To' a
on the back and and make a hole in the top with your hole punch.

4. Thread the label onto a short piece of ribbon and use sticky tape to attach it to your present. Beautiful!

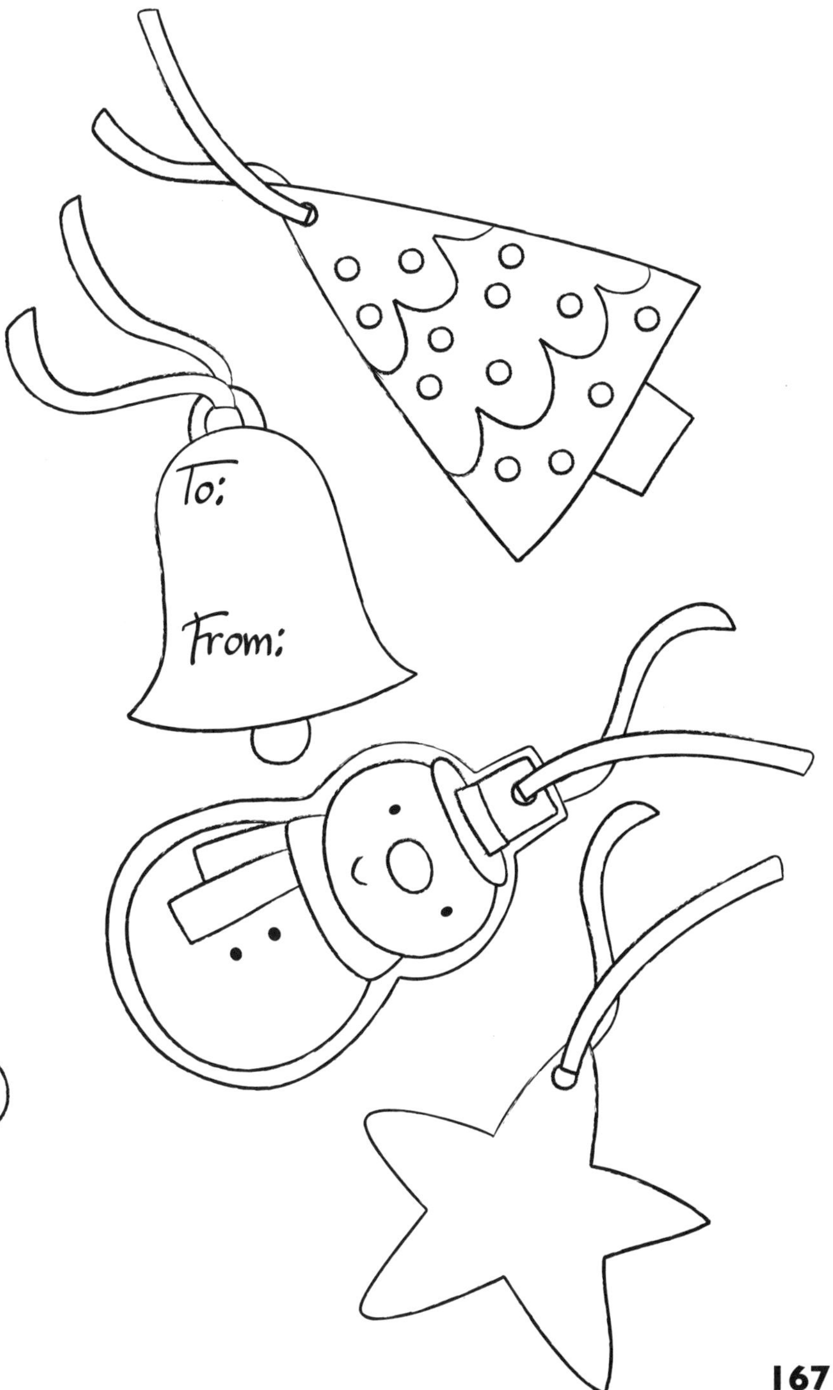

SALT-DOUGH DECORATIONS

Decorate your room, or even your Christmas tree, with these doll and dino creations that you can keep forever!

You will need

- Paper
- pencil
- scissors
- large bowl
- spoon
- 150 g salt
- 300 g plain flour, plus extra for dusting
- 150 ml water
- rolling pin
- table knife
- garlic press
- paints
- paintbrushes
- PVA glue
- ribbon.

1. Trace over the template of the doll or dinosaur on the next page with paper and a pencil. Cut it out.

2. Ask an adult to preheat your oven to its lowest temperature.

Warning! *Make sure you ask an adult to help you whenever you'd like to use the oven.*

3. Put the salt and flour into a large bowl and mix together. Add a little water at a time, stirring continuously until you have a smooth dough that you can squash with your hands. If your dough feels too sticky, add a sprinkle more flour. If it feels too dry and keeps cracking, add a splash more water.

4. Dust your surface and rolling pin with flour. Roll out your dough until it is 1.5 cm thick. Place your template onto the dough and cut around it with a table knife. Cut as many decorations as you can.

5. Use a pencil to make a hole in the top of each decoration, as shown on the template.

6. Use the leftover dough to add detail to your decorations. Push some dough through a garlic press to make hair for your dolls, or cut out small triangles to make scales for your dinos. Stick your detail on using a little water.

7. Place them on a baking tray and ask an adult to put them in the oven for 3–4 hours, or until firm. Remove and leave to cool.

8. Paint your decorations bright colours. Once dry, apply a coat of PVA glue for a shiny finish.

9. Thread your ribbon through the hole in your decorations and secure with a knot. Hang them up or give as gifts.

ON THE SLOPES

The snow is falling in Aviemore! How many people are skiing, snowboarding and sledging? Colour them in as you count them.

How many did you spot?

Skiers 5

Snowboarders 4

Sledgers 5

Runton Road, Poole

Everyone needs to wrap up warmly in the snow...
Give their hats,
scarves and
gloves bright,
cosy designs.

SNOWY SURPRISE

Uh, oh! What's hiding in the snow?

CHRISTMAS CRACKERS

Impress your family this Christmas and make your own Christmas crackers.

For one cracker, you will need

- wrapping paper
- scissors
- 3 x toilet roll tubes
- cracker snap
- sticky tape
- sweets
- glitter
- ribbon.

1. Cut a piece of wrapping paper roughly 33 cm x 17 cm.

2. Tape the cracker snap into the middle of the toilet roll tube and put another tube on either side.

3. Roll the wrapping paper around the tubes and stick it into place with sticky tape.

4. At one end, gently pull one of the tubes out by about 2 cm. Take some ribbon, wrap it around the space created and tie into a bow. This will secure one end of the cracker. Don't tie it too tightly or the paper will tear.

5. Add sweets and glitter to the open end of the cracker. Then repeat step **4** to completely secure the cracker.

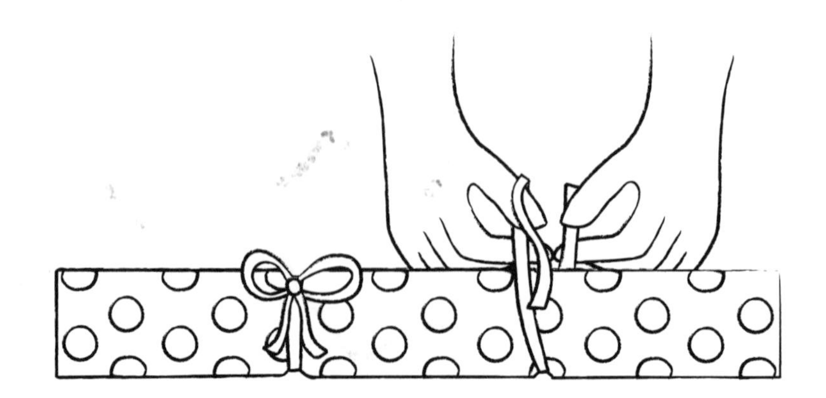

6. Now, remove both tubes at either end.

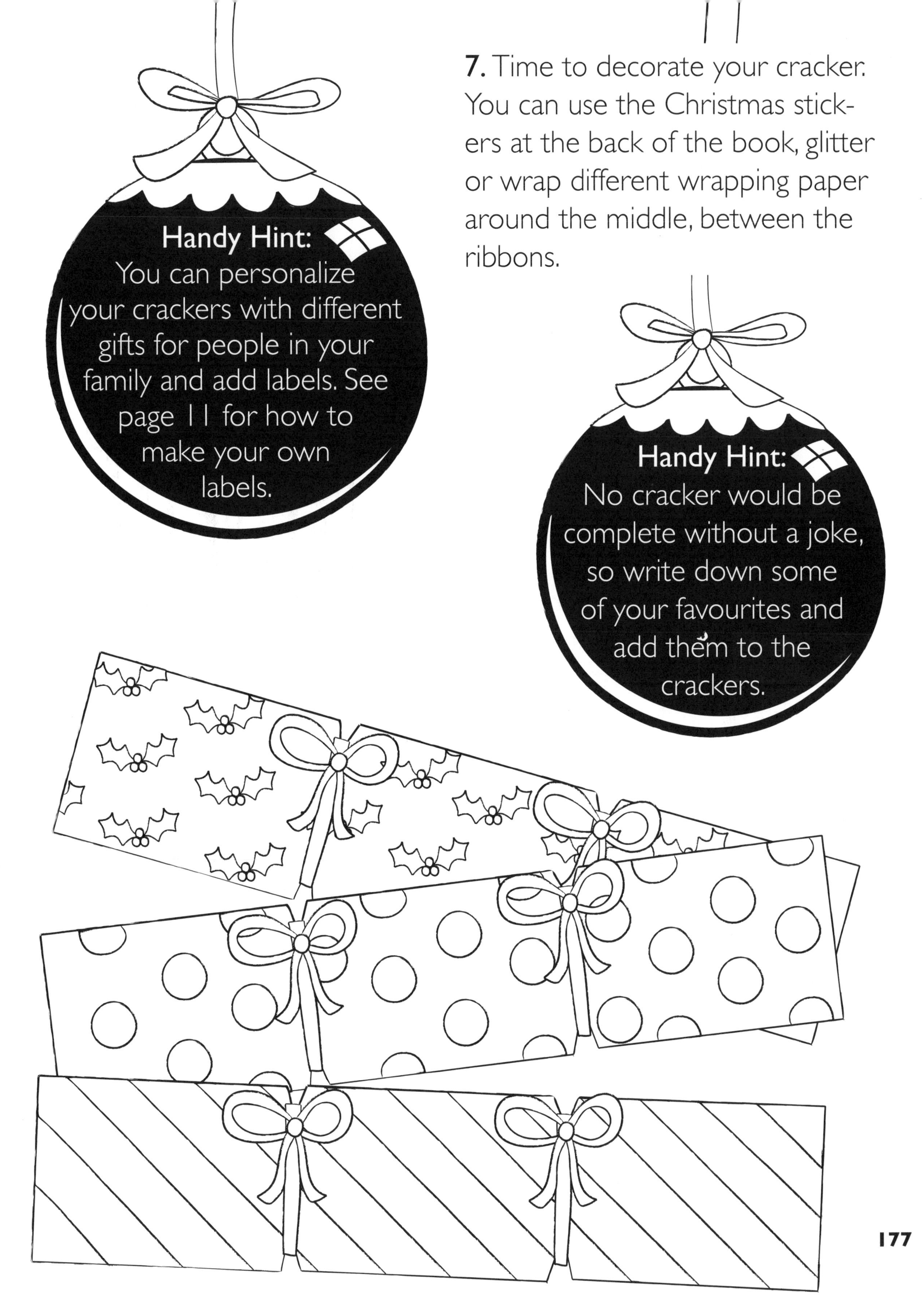

7. Time to decorate your cracker. You can use the Christmas stickers at the back of the book, glitter or wrap different wrapping paper around the middle, between the ribbons.

Handy Hint:
You can personalize your crackers with different gifts for people in your family and add labels. See page 11 for how to make your own labels.

Handy Hint:
No cracker would be complete without a joke, so write down some of your favourites and add them to the crackers.

FESTIVE FUN!

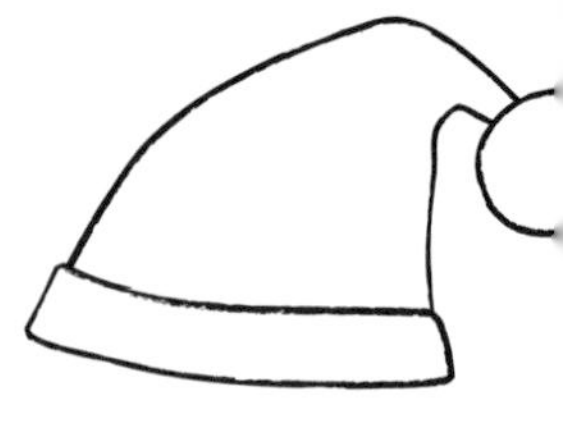

These simple games are great fun for all the family. Just follow the instructions to get into the competitive Christmas spirit.

The Hat Game

You will need

- 4+ players
- paper
- a pen
- a hat
- a timer.

1. Everyone must write down five names and put them into the hat – they can be celebrities, cartoon characters, family or friends.

2. Divide into teams. The team with the youngest person on it goes first. That person is the 'describer'.

3. Round one: set 30 seconds on the timer. The describer picks a name from the hat and describes it to their team without saying the name, any letters or what it sounds like. Once their team guesses who it is, the describer repeats this as many times as they can before the time runs out.

4. Write down your score and it's the next team's turn. Each team takes a turn until there are no names left in the bag, changing describer each time.

Important: If you run out of names on your turn, pause the timer and the same team starts the next round using the rest of the time on the clock.

5. Round two: all of the names go back into the hat and you play again. Except this time the describer can only say one word. Continue until you've guessed all the names, keeping score as you go.

6. Round three: put all the names back in the hat. In this round you can't speak and you have to mime the people like in charades.

7. When you've finished round three, the winner is the team who has the highest score.

Chocolate mint game

The aim of the game is to get the chocolate mint from your fore-head into your mouth without using your hands. The first person to do it wins – simple!

Pass the orange

Separate into two teams and get each team to stand in a line. The first team to pass the orange from one end of the line to the other, without dropping it, wins. The catch is you're not allowed to use your hands. The easiest way to pass it is by holding the orange under your chin and putting it under the next person's chin.

Finish off the delicious Christmas dinner and colour it in.

YULETIDE TEASERS

Test your family's festive knowledge this Christmas with these tricky questions.

1. Which reindeer helps pull Father Christmas's sleigh?
a. Chancer
b. Glancer
c. Prancer

2. What do you traditionally leave out for Rudolph on Christmas Eve?
a. Chocolate
b. A carrot
c. Brussels sprouts

3. What do naughty children traditionally receive for Christmas?
a. A bunch of bananas
b. A lump of coal
c. A pile of gold

4. What is the French word for Christmas?
a. Noël
b. Liam
c. Frank

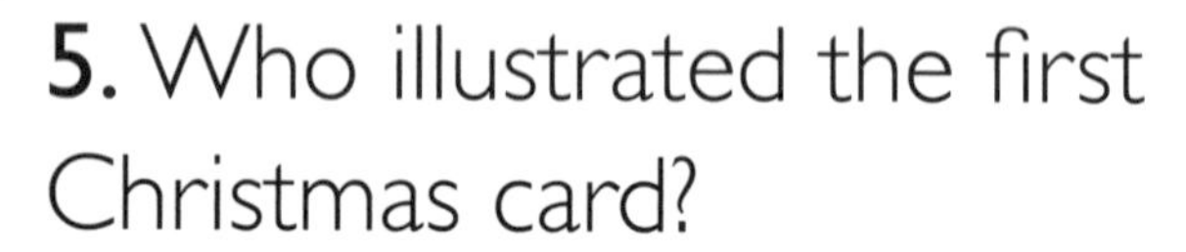

5. Who illustrated the first Christmas card?
a. Quentin Blake
b. John Callott Horsley
c. Pablo Picasso

6. Where does Father Christmas live?
a. The South Pole
b. Northampton
c. The North Pole

7. In the song, The Twelve Days of Christmas, what is given on the fifth day?
a. Five gold rings
b. Five rubber rings
c. Five diamond rings

8. Where do penguins come from?
a. The South Pole
b. The North Pole
c. The zoo

MINCE PIES

Christmas wouldn't be Christmas without a warm mince pie.
This year, why not try making your own?

Ingredients

- 300 g shortcrust pastry
- 1 x 175 g jar mincemeat
- 1 egg, beaten
- 1 tbsp icing sugar
- a little flour, for dusting.

Equipment

- Small bowl
- fork, to beat the eggs
- rolling pin
- 10 cm circular cutter
- 12-hole bun tin
- teaspoon
- 7 cm circular cutter
- pastry brush.

1. Ask an adult to preheat your oven to 200°C/gas mark 6.

2. Sprinkle flour onto your work surface and rolling pin. Roll out your pastry until it is 3 mm thick.

3. Use a 10 cm circular cutter to cut out 12 pastry circles.

Warning! *Make sure you ask an adult to help you whenever you'd like to use the oven.*

4. Place your pastry circles into a 12-hole bun tin, pressing each one gently into place.

5. Use a teaspoon to place a blob of mincemeat onto each circle.

6. Use a 7 cm circular cutter to cut 12 lids from the rest of your pastry. Place a circle on top of each of your pies. Brush with egg.

7. Ask an adult to put them in the oven for 10–15 minutes.

8. Sprinkle with icing sugar and serve warm. Delicious!

BRIGHTON PIER

BRITISH BRILLIANCE

Over the centuries brilliant inventors from England, Scotland and Wales have done their bit to make Britain great. Can you draw a line from each invention to the correct country?

Tarmac

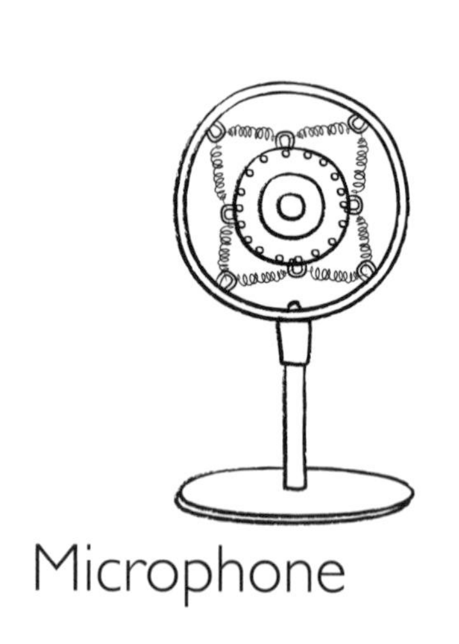

Microphone

Telephone

Modern toothbrush

Wales

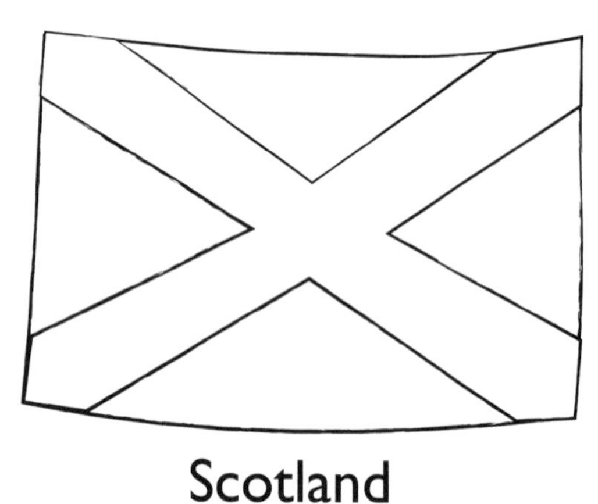

Scotland

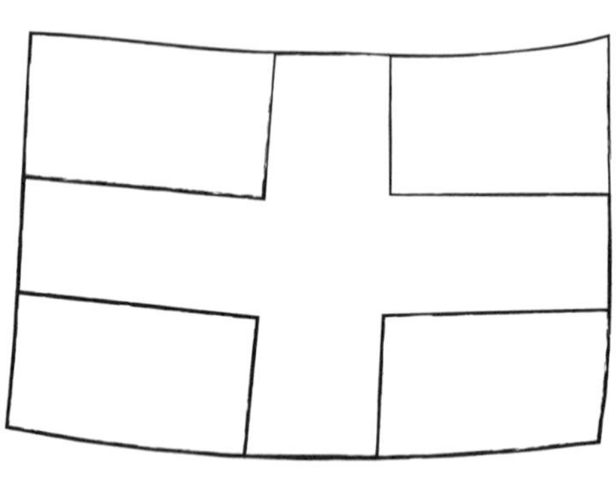

England

The +, - and = signs

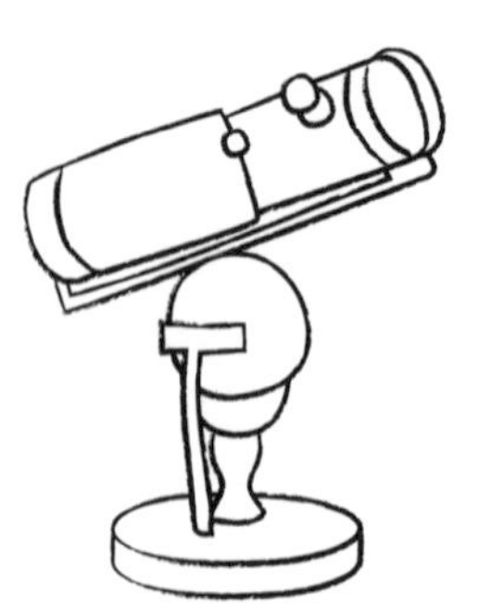

Reflecting telescope

Wind-up radio

Television

ALL THE ANSWERS

All the Fun of the Fair! pages 12 and 13

Dragon Quest page 40

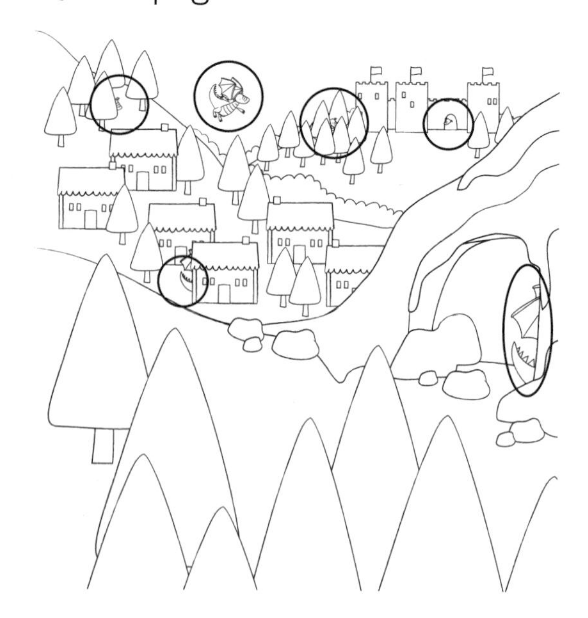

Toot Toot! pages 26 and 27

Hidden Rock Puzzle page 67

Hot Cross Maze page 37

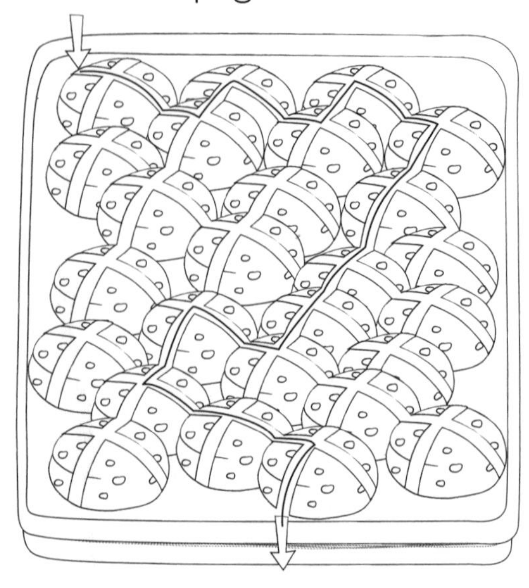

Party Puzzler pages 76 and 77
The hats were left at number 3.

What a Mess page 79

Festival Fun pages 82 and 83

Puzzling Places page 92
They're all real!

Which Knight is Right? page 121
Sir Gawain is circled
The two identical knights are highlighted in grey.

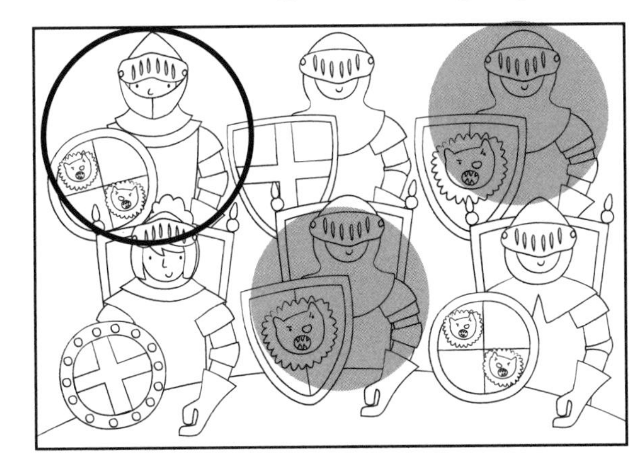

Spooky Spots pages 126 and 127

Baker Puzzle page 129
Anna won first place, Toby won second place and RJ was the runner up.

Dot-to-dot page 136
It's a baker!

Save the Queen! page 139

Spend the day at Windsor Castle pages 148 and 149

Theatreland! pages 150 and 151

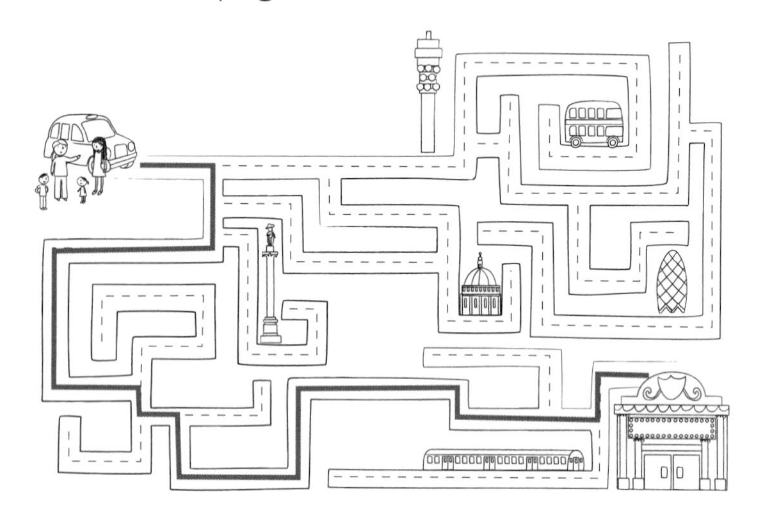

Hot Samosas Wordsearch page 153

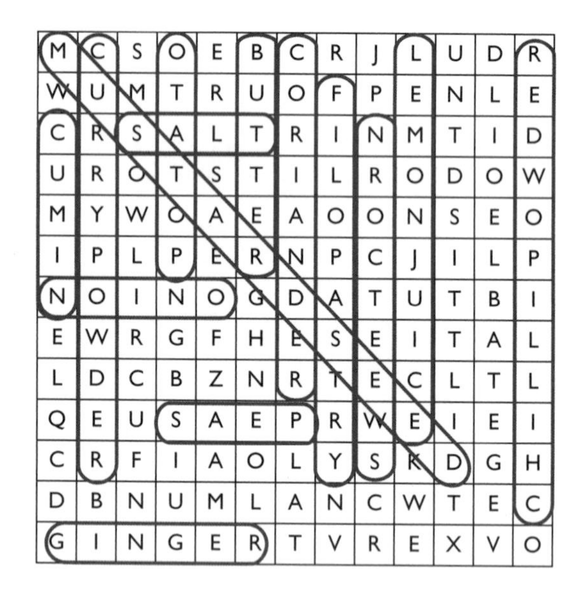

Bara Brith Sudoku page 161

Woodland Maze page 163

Somerset House Skaters pages 164 and 165

On the Slopes pages 170 and171

5 Skiers

4 Snowboarders

5 Sledgers

Snowy surprise page 175

It's a Welsh dragon!

Yuletide Teasers page 182

1. c) Prancer
2. b) A carrot
3. b) A lump of coal
4. a) Noël
5. b) John Callott Horsley
6. c) The North Pole
7. a) Five gold rings
8. a) The South Pole

British Brilliance page 186

Welsh inventions

Microphone by David Edward Hughes
The +, - and = signs by Robert Recorde

Scottish inventions

Television by John Logie Baird
Tarmac by John MacAdam
Telephone by Alexander Graham Bell

English inventions

Wind-up radio by Trevor Baylis
Reflecting telescope by Isaac Newton
Modern toothbrush by William Addis

ALSO AVAILABLE

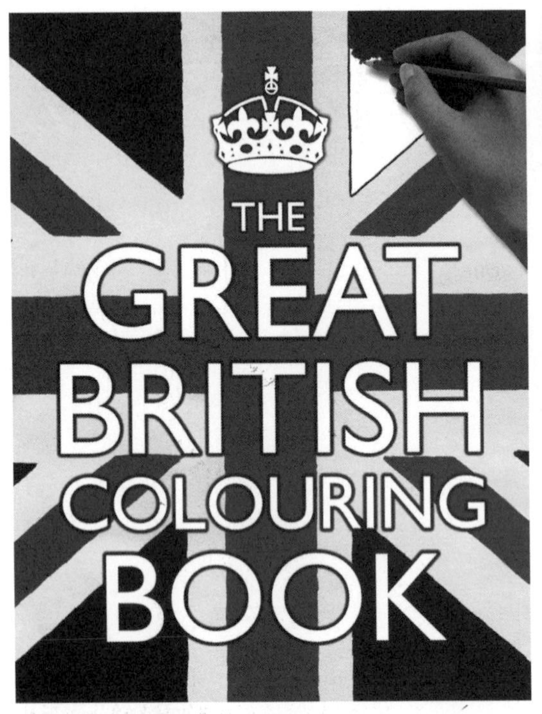

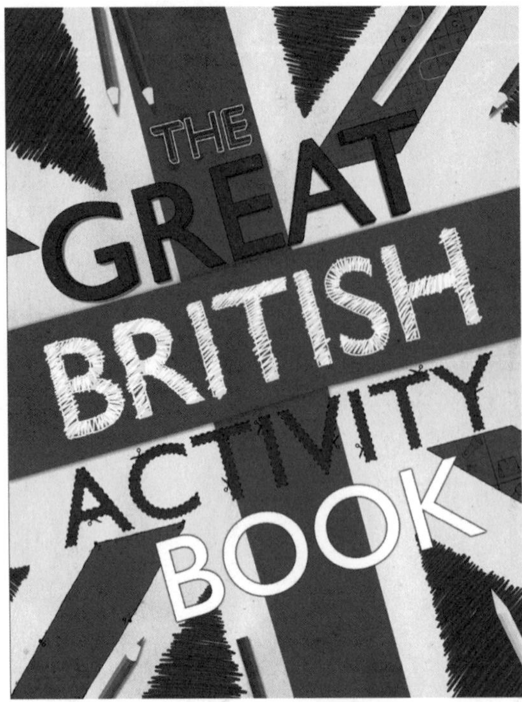

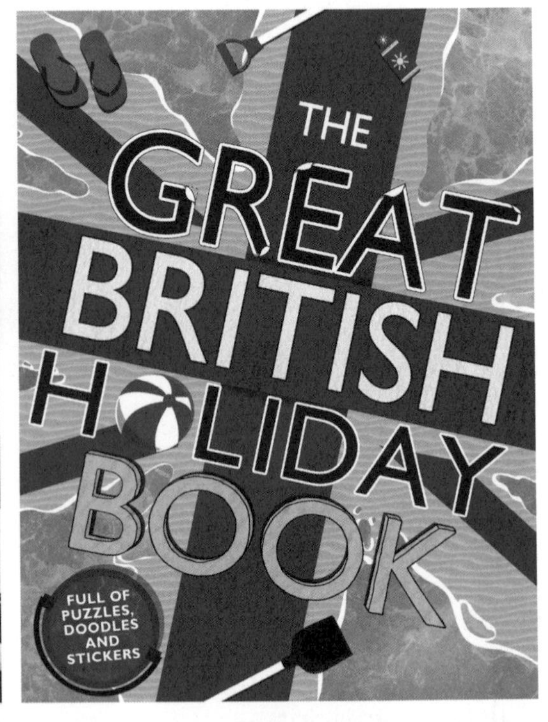

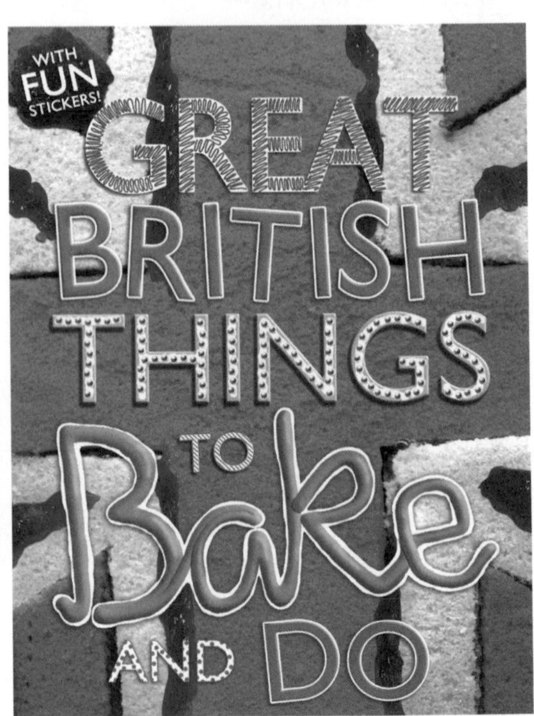